f4

ᅴ ᄂ

THE ISLAND

ARTHUR GUIRDHAM

The Island

JERSEY
NEVILLE SPEARMAN

First published in Great Britain 1980 by
Neville Spearman (Jersey) Limited
PO Box 75, Normandy House, St Helier, Jersey
Channel Islands

Distributed by Neville Spearman Limited
The Priory Gate, Friars Street, Sudbury
Suffolk

ISBN 0 85978 039 2

Text set 10/12 pt Plantin Roman by
Galleon Photosetting, Ipswich
and printed and bound by
REDWOOD BURN LIMITED
Trowbridge & Esher

INTRODUCTION

In my books The Cathars and Reincarnation *and* We Are One Another *I converted myself into an amateur historian to verify obscure facts mostly provided by others. By such means I have convinced myself of the truth of reincarnation. Both of these books were concerned with my life as a Cathar. In* The Lake And The Castle *I went a step further and learnt of my Roman, Celtic and Napoleonic incarnations through a series of synchronizations involving the living and the discarnates. In a word, the type of books I wrote kept pace with my psychic development. This latest book describing my incarnation on an island off Crete is a straight and uncomplicated example of far memory. Writing it I was not dependent on the help of the living or the discarnates who indeed offered no aid in composition. After it was finished the revenants who had shared several incarnations with me and who at different times demanded of me so much hard work in the verification of obscure facts, testified to the authenticity of my story.*

This is not a visionary work. All I have written I have seen and remembered.

1

I REMEMBER the whiteness of the house and the openness to the sun so that in the Mid-summer we were grateful for the porch with the two columns that looked on the low hills strewn with rocks with between them a mat of thyme always humming with bees and in the Summer so purple that you saw the fire in the earth long after the sundown. On this hill was written the story of all that happened in my first years. There was first the crocuses in Spring, very white at the summit in the shade of the rocks. Afterwards there was the intermittent snowfall of the almonds in blossom and under the almonds the grass flushed with anemones, a milder purple than the thyme and with all the wakefulness and timidity of morning. Before the first heat there was the flame and foredoomed splendour of the rock roses, each flower fading in a day even in the mildness of Spring. With the coming of the Summer there was, even on days when the clouds beat up from the sea, the perpetual sunshine where the broom was blooming. It was so profuse and intensely gay that it dispersed shadows near it. After the broom, with the great heat, there were no colours but the azure of the sky and the deep, reflective blue of the sea below it and, on the hill, the smouldering world of small shrubs with sharp odours and dark colours and the mysterious sensation that time had stopped.

This feeling that time had stopped was important to me. It was for this reason that the Summer was a delight and a torture. With the sensation of the sun at anchor, of death being suspended, there was a deep happiness but with it the fear that for a moment I would be separated from the world and that people would notice my difference from others. The attacks were brief. One moment there was the hill with the single arbutus, with its red flaked bark and burnished leaves leaning away from the sea wind. Next there was nothing and when I returned to myself the world was trembling. Then I traced this tremor to my own limbs and lowered my arm which was raised towards my shoulder. The harsh disjointed throbbing ceased in my brain. I never fell in these attacks which were no trouble to me unless they were noticed by others. They came always with the feeling that time had altered. If I were alone this feeling would last for minutes. I could see, flaming and alive around the petals of each flower, the shimmer of its soul in something that vibrated in the air around it.

I must have been ten when, after one of these attacks, my father took me to the wise man Personides who lived in the house beyond the inlet to the South and over the hill, further East than our own and which was black at sundown. What I remember most of this journey was passing the lake of still water in the hollow of the hill. There was the outlet to the sea and the ripple of blue waves but on the landward side the water was still and though there were no overlapping rocks there was somehow the darkness of night upon it. The surface was broken by the fleshy leaves of the water lilies. I could not say why they made me shiver. They were immobile, watchful and avaricious. It seemed to me that in their immobility they sucked out what was good in the water through their curled remorseless lips. I could not understand how the flowers, prodigal as stars scattering their emanations across the vault of night, each pointed petal like the flash of a planet, could arise from such a source. 'Why is the water so black?' I said.

'It looks black because of the plants on its surface. You know she comes here at night.'

'Who?'

'The goddess and huntress. It must be Artemis.' My father was becoming excited. He spoke with the same quavering emphasis as when he discussed things with his friends. I was to learn later that he combined a desire to be emphatic with a crippling lack of confidence. 'Sometimes, at a time of full moon, it is Aphrodite herself. Once she bathed in the lake.'

'Have you seen her?' I said.

'Well, no,' he answered. When I grew up I learnt that the words 'well, no' could have served as his epitaph.

'Have you ever watched by the lake when the moon was full?'

'No.'

'Then you haven't seen her.'

'But you don't understand. It would not be seemly. Aphrodite is a Goddess.'

I has no idea and little interest in what he meant by seemly. He was very concerned that Aphrodite should not be seen naked. At the same time he was regularly bathed by our women slaves. I had the dim idea that the Gods would only take their clothes off in certain circumstances. It conflicted with what I had heard elsewhere and the statues I had seen. It did not bother me much. My father's conversation always confused me. Perhaps he had a genius for confusing himself.

All I was interested in was what was true. Even in childhood my insistence that things be seen and heard separated me from my fellows. They thought me brusque and even ill mannered.

The wise man lived in a bigger house than my father's. He had dark eyes, pointed face and a grizzled beard. He half smiled when he saw me. He greeted my father in the same way but more listlessly. He seemed to be tired of my father before the interview began.

My father told the story of my attacks and how sometimes I seemed to go from this world, that my eyes became blank but that I never fell. The wise man put his hand on my forehead and held it there for a few moments. I felt that his palms were tingling and that there was great heat in his hands and that my forehead was pulsating. He took his hands away and told me to go. 'It's nothing,' he said. 'There is nothing to be afraid of. You're like us all, like me,

9

like your father. We are all made in different ways and have different ways of showing it.'

I went outside while they talked in the house. I watched the edges of the waves curling to white foam on the shores of the inlet. I looked at the thin channel between the rocks and the near shore of the inlet. I saw the hole in the rocks where people said the oracle had lived. She had told the future and healed the sick. One day she had walked on the thin path scratched in the rock which dwindled to nothing on the seaward side of the point. She had fallen into the water and drowned. I had asked my father why, if she could heal the sick, she had not taught herself to swim. My father thought I was blasphemous.

Now, as I looked at the cave, I saw a woman walking the landward path that fringed the channel and led to the cave. At that distance I could only see that she was tall, erect and that her hair was black. She was no longer a girl but she was strong-legged and her movements were supple. It was surprising to see her there because, while I knew that men and women met in caves elsewhere as well as in the thickets, they avoided this cave because there was something awesome about it. A goat had entered there by accident and had fallen dead in a fit. A girl who had wandered there as a child was described by people as never the same afterwards. Certainly the girl remained strikingly stupid. When I grew up I learnt that on the island all manner of defects of character and intelligence were attributed to spirits. The idea that the stupid very often begat the stupid was rejected as heresy.

When I saw the woman enter the cave the only thought in my head was that she was brave and stupid. I wondered whether she would, on emerging, fall into a fit or the longer tribulation of a slow decline. I had every intention of staying where I was until the woman came out but at that moment my father and Personides both left the house and moved to the porch which faced the coolness of the North and the only real mountain on the island. I could not help hearing my father, 'But of course he is a child of the Gods.'

'How can you call him a child of the Gods simply because he was born as a result of a Dionysian frenzy? Are you saying that you were possessed by a God?' Personides sounded contemptuous.

'No, it could have been the woman,' my father said grudgingly.

'Even if she was taken over when you made love to her it is not to say it was by a Goddess or even a messenger. What was she like?'

'Like?' my father said feebly. 'I can't give you much detail. Transported as I was——'

'Transported——?'

'Well, you know, the religious atmosphere.'

'You had taken some wine?'

'Certainly, you know how it is.'

Personides sighed. 'The woman was not of the island?'

'She came from Crete.'

'The facts are that you had a woman, almost unknown to you, while you were drunk, no, let's say in a religious state – the two may even be the same – and you believe your progeny to be a son of the Gods. You need a little more evidence than that.'

'But in these absences he goes out of time. He may well be among those who see into the future.'

'So do many with his malady.'

'You call it a malady. How would you treat it?'

'Not at all. He may grow out of it. If he doesn't he will come to no harm from it.'

'I would be grateful for some medicine.'

'That would make it worse.'

'I thought——' My father's voice trailed off helplessly.

'That I would be able to help you. I have. But there is no point in cherishing illusions about your son being born of the Gods. Also I have reassured you. I have told you that he will come to no harm – from his malady.'

'What do you mean, from his malady?'

'We all die,' said Personides.

The parting between the wise man and my father was not protracted. The latter was upset and muttering incoherent but venomous phrases about uncultured and false prophets. His voice gained in tone as he spoke of false prophets. He put his arms round me, one of the rare, angular gestures of affection he permitted himself. I knew in that moment that all he was concerned with was what I could be and not what I was.

'A woman has gone into the cave,' I said. I was thinking of my mother and what I said had no meaning except as a gag to my father.

'She must be mad. I expect it's that idiotic girl Electra.'

I knew Electra. She was sixteen and lithe with the muscles of a boy. Her eyes had the incandescent darkness of black grapes and there was no escaping from them. 'It wasn't Electra. It was somebody about twenty years older.'

'Then she's madder than Electra,' he said. 'What did she look like?'

'Not like anyone on the island.'

My father was silent. He seemed more troubled than ever. The pallor spread from his cheeks to below his grey, befogged, unseeing eyes. He was the kind of man who had ideas about everything and saw nothing.

I was not concerned with the woman in the cave. All I thought of was my mother but I was determined not to ask my father about her. He had certainly told me that she had died in childbirth and, though nothing I had heard in my father's talk with Personides spoke to the contrary, I knew it was all a lie. I waited till night when my father was asleep. I tiptoed to the shed where Nikita slept with her daughter Thekla. Nikita threw off a woollen wrap which was a blanket to her at night and a garment by day. With her broad shoulders and hips, her huge, pyramidal, outward pointed breasts and her swollen belly, she looked like a village fête concept of an ancient Goddess of fertility. Her face was white and broad-boned. She came from somewhere north of Thrace. Her eyes were a washed-out grey. Sometimes, narrowing intently, they aspired to an artificial warmth. I did not like her at all. She was mistress as well as slave to my father. I think he took her because it would be remiss and uneconomical to forgo her.

Her daughter Thekla was sleeping in a corner with her back turned to us. That was something to be thankful for. I was in love with Thekla in a dreamy, half reverent, half seminal manner. There were stirrings of desire in my love for her but I was still in that state of first innocence when her beauty meant more than the pains it aroused.

Nikita dragged her woollen wrap round her and we slipped into the night. 'Who was my mother?' I said. She half closed her eyelids, concentrating hard in order to be compassionate. 'You poor lamb, you know already. Your mother died in childbed to give you birth.'

'She didn't.'

'Who's been telling you lies?' What a cruel thing to tell a child lies about his lost mother.'

12

'That's what you have been doing for years.'

'Not me, not me.'

'Come, tell me,' I said.

'Not here, not now.'

'When?' I said.

'Tomorrow in your bedchamber.' She went back to her hut.

The next night I lay awake waiting for her. I thought she was afraid. I went to the door and looked out into the night. The moon was anchored in the sky and the stars were low. I could see their reflection in the sea. It was a strange feeling to wait, under the blue tapestry of a sky scattered with stars, for a woman as repellent as Nikita. The night was windless. There was no sound from the sea. Its murmur died behind the pale rocks that poured, in a silent cascade, from the slope of the hill to the enigmatic waters of the inlet. I heard for a moment the singing that lives in the heart of silence. Then I went back to my room, knowing that the hag was not coming. I fell asleep and woke in the small hours with her lying beside me. When she knew I was awake she rolled on her side and locked me in her arms. I was half suffocated by the amplitude of her breasts and the intensity of my revulsion for her. 'Your mother, my dove——'

'Tell me quickly.'

'If I tell you your father will throw me out.'

'My father will not know.'

'Your mother came from Crete. Your father only met her for a night. It was of course completely respectable. It was the feast of Dionysius. You know what happens.'

'Yes.'

'You have never had a woman?'

'No. Get on with the story.'

'It is all quite simple. Your mother went back to Crete. As I said, she was a respectable, well brought up girl of rich parents. I mean no offence if I say much richer than your father. When she discovered she would have a child she wished to hide from her parents, above all because a marriage had been arranged for her. She came here to have the child. After she had had it she went back to Crete. She left you to my care.'

I looked at Nikita, at her slab-like face, at the voluminous moonlit haze of her breasts and I heard her breathing beside me. It was

13

obvious that there were things for which I could never forgive my mother. 'Why didn't she keep me beside her in Crete?'

'Without a father, without even the name of a father! I tell you that your mother was a respectable woman. I got to know her well when I nursed her here.'

'Thank you,' I said. 'And now you can go.'

'You did say you had never had a woman.'

'Yes.'

'It seems wrong somehow. You are over fourteen.'

'You had better go back,' I said.

2

IN the two years that followed I thought much about my mother. From Nikita's descriptions I have the impression of a soft faced woman – with melting brown eyes but I knew that no picture could be made of these fictional data. Nikita was a rock-hard woman with the need to sentimentalize life and make it possible for herself and others. I never dreamt of asking my father. I knew that from him, for different reasons, I would obtain an equally idealized and falsified picture. It would be necessary for him to paint my mother in beautiful colours because of the degree to which he had failed her.

I could not expel from my mind the memory of the woman I had seen entering the cave. I asked many people if they had done so but all shrank from the question. For some the mere suggestion smacked of coarse impiety. The cave had been occupied by an oracle and to them it was still a sanctuary. Others assumed that the woman had malign powers. I think most people believed this to some extent. What was the use of an oracle without the power to defend herself and her place of habitation? If she were to do so must she not always be blessed with the power to strike quickly and lethally? The people in the island expected good and bad of their Gods, the messengers of the Gods and also the oracles. They saw them as like themselves but with powers enhanced. The goodness of common man was therefore greater in the Gods and the evil equally augmented. Certainly nobody went near the cave. Though I was mysteriously drawn to it I did not go there myself.

At that time I had on several successive nights a strange and simple dream. On those nights in which the dream came to me I suffered attacks in which my mind emptied and I came to with my right hand raised towards my shoulder. It was as if I needed this break in consciousness to allow more light to pierce a curtain which hung inside me. In the sleep which followed these attacks I saw a girl with light hair and eyes coloured with the blue below the surface of the sea. Her wide mouth was smiling and her hands were raised in welcome. Her breasts were bare in the fashion of the Cretan nobility. She wore a skirt slung from her shoulders by two narrow bands. When she lifted up her hands her breasts tightened and rose with them. Her skirt was gold, deeper gold than her hair. She spoke one sentence only, 'I come to you and I come to stay.' I had seen the same picture and heard the same words not only in dreams but by day in visions. The dream and the vision never varied and I knew beyond doubt that I would see her soon. I do not know why I knew. Certainly I asked no one about it. My knowing that what I thought was true was part of the same process which enabled me to see her coming forward in a dream and over the hills in the light of morning.

While I never mentioned the dream to my father I told him that regularly I dreamt and saw things before they happened. I did not ask my father for advice or information. I knew he was a pretentious windbag but in talking to him I gained something. He knew so many things and talked of them with such unceasing fervour that among the debris of his conversation I could find something of value, not because it came from my father but because it fitted into the pattern of thought with which I was concerned. Also and always I wished to know the truth. This was the name I gave to what governed my life from the depths of my being. My father also claimed to be a seeker of the truth. The difference was that he called it philosophy. This meant for him the collection and annexation of every comforting statement and illusion he had ever heard. Truth for him was a matter of addition. For me it was subtraction. We were born like that and there was an unbridgeable gulf between us.

One day on a sharp Winter morning when the leaves on the olives were brittle and silver I asked my father about the Gods. It was

15

fitting that it should be Winter and the land asleep because with the coming of Spring, and straight through the Summer to the falling asleep at the Winter solstice, I was outside the home occupied with affairs which were hard to define. I spent my days wandering and watching and feeling. Life for me was a matter of immediate sensation and intensive watching. In a word I was alive in all the layers of my being. I was too happy to know my own joy. My sole disquiet was to see into the future and the past. When I first looked backwards I thought that what I saw were waking dreams and then pages built from all I had seen in the years of childhood but I learnt later that most of what we think we imagine has happened before, sometimes to ourselves and sometimes to others. What we call imagination was something seen when we wandered in the shadows of a strange forgotten world. I did not know yet that these lost worlds were my own lives. I thought they were memories suspended within the mist which hovers between birth and infancy.

'The greatest God of all is Zeus,' said my father.

'What does he do?'

'Presides over the other Gods.'

'Is that all?'

'It is enough for any God.'

'Why, are the Gods tired?' I said. 'What does he do for us?'

'He presides over the other Gods who are in closer contact with us and who can help us more. There is Demeter, the Goddess of the harvest. What she does for us is obvious. That is why we sacrifice to her.'

'You mean we sacrifice to her because she does things for us?'

'Not to do so would be to lack gratitude.' My father always expressed himself best when his case was weakest.

'We also sacrifice beforehand to make sure she does it.'

'That is only reasonable but you express yourself coarsely.'

'Last year the rain fell at the wrong time and the harvest was bad. Did we not sacrifice enough?'

'I personally sacrificed more than was required,' said my father. 'The explanation is that Zeus was angry.'

'With whom and for what?'

'A mood,' said my father and then, inflated by his originality, added with confidence, 'A divine mood, of course.'

'So the Gods have emotions like us?'

16

'No, bigger, much bigger emotions,' said my father vaguely but with desperation.

'Couldn't Demeter have intervened with Zeus for us? You say she is nearer to us and can help us more. Has she feelings like us?'

'She is of divine origin but she shows her feelings.'

'She can't have been always divine if she shows her feelings.'

'The Gods visit the earth occasionally out of their kindness to share our feelings and emotions.'

'How can they know our feelings if they have never lived?'

'Because they are Gods,' said my father testily.

'Did Dionysius ever live?'

My father went red and pale and a number of colours between the two. 'You could say that he lives in our hearts but he is essentially a God.'

'He particularly is very close to us,' I said. I looked intently at my father and thought of my mother, of Nikita, of other women in the island and possibly Thekla. I hoped he would leave Thekla alone.

'Very close indeed,' my father muttered thickly.

'How did Apollo come to Greece?' I asked.

'He arrived across the sea from Rhodes on the back of a dolphin.'

'Does that prove he is a God?'

'With other things, yes.'

'That's odd,' I said. 'Do you know that many days I sit on the tongue of rock from the East bay and play my flute to the dolphins? They feed out of my hand and sit with me for hours. I believe they have a brain like a man and we can speak to them through music. I have stroked the head of a dolphin for as long as you take to eat a meal. I believe I could train a dolphin to carry me on its back around the island.'

'I suppose you are out of your mind.'

'If you give me six months I will show you that this is possible.'

'What is the point dedicating six months to an act of blasphemy?'

'Nothing, it is just that I would ride on a dolphin's back like Apollo. It is just that I believe that all these Gods and Goddesses were once strong or clever men or very beautiful women and that we make stories about them.'

'I tell you they and their messengers have the power of visiting us on earth.' My father tried to snarl but all that happened was that his nostrils widened.

'If after death they visit us on earth they are only lost people. They are lost in the shades and need our comfort.'

'You yourself are lost,' said my father. He walked away with his head bent and all of a sudden I was sorry for him. He believed me to be a son of the Gods. His ambition for me was that I should be an intermediary between them and men. He built it all on my seeing into the future and not that I had been conceived in a Dionysian frenzy. However much I was sorry for my father I could only see him with his normally pale face engorged and his harassed forehead encircled with vine leaves. He had the mind of a fidgety and muddled woman, an immense absorbent capacity for what he called wisdom and which was only folklore, and an incongruous sexuality which he somehow contrived to regard as sacred. Perhaps he was vital. Perhaps he was right, I was not his son but a progeny of the Gods. I say this not with pride but to account for a discrepancy.

Some nights after this conversation with my father I was tense and restless and the moon was high. It was often like that with the fullness of the moon. It was all to do with my seeing into the future. What I saw were trivial things but once I saw a ship sinking and when this happened I was stricken because I had done nothing to save it. What could I do? The ship came from an island South of Crete. I saw the port it sailed from and the tempest rising but I did not know from my waking knowledge its track on the sea and its destination. Because on this particular night, with the moon high, I feared an attack and with it some future disaster I was powerless to prevent, I stole out of the house at midnight. For a moment I looked at the hut where Thekla was sleeping. Thekla was short and slim but with my mind running ahead of my breathing life I saw her at forty, distended into the semblance of her mother, huge, columnar thighs, pert, fecund stomach, the outward pointing missiles of her huge breasts and a dark stubble of hair on her upper lip which was a laughable denial of her over-ripe feminity added by one of the more malicious Gods with a taste for caricature. Thekla was small and slender but the broad face which, in her mother, was like a lascivious tombstone, was mobile and frank and seemed the extension of a wide smile born in her generous mouth. Her hair was dark bronze. It was burnished and crinkled like beech leaves in Autumn. Her dark brown eyes were a kind summons and her body a gift but not yet given. I felt sure that my father had not yet asserted his rights. I

18

would surely have recognized the anticipatory hypocrisies and insane, effervescent kindnesses showered on all his circle preceding their seduction.

Suddenly I had an irresistible desire to get Thekla and take her with me. I was sure I could rely on the connivance of her mother. It was in her interest to keep on good terms with two generations of employers. I saw myself with my arm round Thekla, going between the aromatic shrubs, their leaves blanched with the moonlight, their inner, intricate branches intensely dark. I longed that Thekla would not grow like her mother. More than that I yearned to be the first to know her. All my will and all the rising sap in the tree within me led me to the hut in which Thekla was sleeping. Nevertheless I moved lightly past it, beyond my will. A marsh light was glowing in my brain. I followed it not because of what it intimated to my senses but because of the tug of its irresistible current in my deepest tissues.

I went along the track I had taken when I went with my father to the wise man Personides the day my father wished to elevate my illness to the level of divinity. I could see the sea to the right and the flat fan of reflected moonlight laid across its still waters. I saw the flickering tongue of the inlet probing the darkness of the earth. Then the inlet ceased suddenly and what was merely the half darkness of earth, frosted by moonlight, was inky and opaque. As I came closer I saw that this was the pool of water lilies but the flowers were not open and the flat, over-succulent leaves intensified the darkness of the water which engulfed them. It was silent as death, without motion or music. It all seemed insulated against the light of the moon, to be lifeless and void, a kind of evil negation of light and air. Then suddenly I saw not the lilies opening but the stars of night reflected in the water. I wondered why I had not seen them before. A low cloud passed over the moon and stars. Why were the constellations so low in the sky and what was the light that moved on the waters?

Then the circle of light that moved on the waters formed into a face and then a face with two eyes set widely on her forehead. Her forehead was blinding white. Some of its radiance came from the diamond on the filet which circled her brow, but mostly she herself was luminous and the incandescent lightness which poured from her head increased when I saw her shoulders and breasts. Then the colour of her hair intensified. It was deep gold so that what I saw was a pattern of gold and silver. Her eyes were green gold like Spring leaves darkened by the unbreathing and heavy greenness of Summer. I turned away from her because my eyes were aching.

She was standing beside me. She was naked as I had seen her in a statue but as real as Thekla. Her eyes were smiling and I looked from them to the diamond on her forehead. 'That is right for the beginning,' she said. 'You looked from me to the brightness of the diamond. The diamond is the truth attained. I wear it because I myself am still unfinished,' she said. 'Touch my body.'

'Where?'

'Anywhere you wish. How could there be wrong when there is no flesh?'

I moved my hand towards her heart, below her left breast. I passed through a zone of air like drifting, frozen feathers. Then I moved it up her body below the level of her breasts. My forehead was bursting with the thought in my head. 'Say it,' she said. 'All your future depends on saying it quickly.'

'So you do come back and the Goddesses return?'

'Yes. Now that you have said it and felt it, it is a thought no more but a truth which will be with you always.'

'So my father was right?'

'No, altogether wrong.'

'Explain it to me.'

'No, never,' she said. 'You cannot go back to explanations. Truth is what you have lived. Do you doubt I am here beside you?'

'No.'

'Tell me my name.' There was no note of command in her voice. There was a faint breathlessness, perhaps even a hint of supplication.

'Artemis.'

'Now you have said it we say farewell.'

'Let me look at you longer. I cannot bear you to leave me. I cannot bear to forget you.'

'You cannot. It is not a matter of time or memory. It is only reality. I am going now. Listen carefully to what is the last I can say. You will never see me again. This was a necessary revelation. You had all the power to know and you refuse to know.'

'Like my father?'

'Your father is a waking dream. You are on a different plane but

20

encumbered by the rags of reason. See, feel and hear. The Gods return.'

'Return,' I said. 'Once you lived on earth?'

'Does that need an answer? Why should we return if we have never lived?'

I could feel the agony of her going. A great cloud of anguish came up from behind and the shadow of its wings enfolded my temples. 'Now you have come I can't live without you. Was it right to come if you meant to go?'

Now her smile was more solemn. 'There is much to learn but others will help you. There are some much nearer the earth. I will send them to you. I come here to stab you with longings you cannot fulfil. You will see me again but only after death.* Others will come from me and sometimes you will feel my presence. Someone else will be coming soon.'

I looked at her once again from the halo glistening above her hair to the line of her breasts and her supple flanks. Then she was gone and the stars gone out. They were reflected no more in the lake and I knew then that where there has been great light it attracts great darkness and that around every shrine where a Goddess has been a fury is lurking. I knew that where great good penetrated within you the faintness and sickness which follows is the onrush of evil into what has been left empty by the searching intensity and the light which has preceded it.

I lay by the lake till morning. I folded my cloak about me. The earth was cold with the weariness of the moon dragging to daylight and with it its tissues clogged by the torpor of Winter. I could feel the heat in my body thawing out the coldness of the earth about me. It was as though I were dead and was warming my own grave with an inexplicable incandescence derived from the decomposition of my body. When the stars went out I went back home. Thekla was already at the door of her hut. She looked tender and bewildered. 'I have been out all night,' I said.

'I know.'

'How do you know?'

'I think about you.'

* I saw her again somewhere between AD 1814 and 1820 at the mouth of an alley in Cracow. This time I saw her in a dream in 1975. In the dream she came back as Diana the Huntress. Diana is the Roman name for Artemis.

'Why?'

'I don't know.' Thekla was seventeen at that time. She seemed younger than I was and desperately tender.

I knew that what I had seen was not only unforgettable but real. I knew the truth was, with no effort of my own, being built inside me. I knew also that in a way this was an experience from which I would never recover, that the rest of my life and, as I learnt later, for the rest of my lives, I would move peering between the colonnades of time for the return of Artemis. But as the days lengthened and the winter died, and as she who was promised did not appear, I gave up hope and told myself that I had had my one and only revelation. It was a kind of sustenance on which I was intended to live until I lay in my stone sarcophagus within sight of the sea but not hearing its murmur.

3

WITH the coming of Spring I walked up the hill in front of the house. In the sharp hush of Winter the cliffs fell thin-edged and pale to the moaning clamour of the sea. Now the clouds had moved North to the mountains of Greece and the air about me was crystalline and taut and vibrated with the unrelenting murmur of the waves. I felt in my ears the twanging of lute strings not plucked by fingers but trembling in the wind.

I was twenty paces from the top of the hill when I saw her crossing the skyline. She came towards me as in my dreams, hand raised, breasts naked, her blue eyes shining and her full lips widening still further to kiss me.

I kissed her briefly. I was only a boy and compared with those around me lacking in virility. Or was it that the world of vision had come to me before the life of desires and longings? Was I older or younger than the boys of the same age on the island? Though our kiss was brief it was unforgettable and all possessing. The curious thing is that there was nothing warm about it. I felt on my lips the cold exhilaration of mountain water and then, in the pit of my stomach between my arching ribs, the thin, immeasurably deep stab of a fine needle. Though I had never seen her before there was no constraint between us. The first thought that came to my head was that we need not explain ourselves to each other.

We sat on the lee of the hill caressed by the sun in the warm light of Spring, with its sharply descending sheets of white light unblurred by the infiltration of the molten gold of Summer. We were hidden by the rock roses that grew, when we were standing, as high as our waists and which made the air a zone of trembling purple which came and went with an aura about us. 'I wished to come sooner,' she said.

'I expected you earlier. I waited for you the night after I saw the Goddess by the lake and she said she would send a messenger. I haven't told you about the Goddess.'

'I have seen her,' she said. She spoke calmly and naturally, as though what she spoke of was not an event.

'You see her often?' I asked.

'I saw her once, the same night as you did.'

'What did she say?'

'That I must go to see you.' She rolled away from me on her left side. Her right arm moved away from me as she plucked at a sprig of mint lying on her left side under her head so that it was crushed by her breast and the sharpness of the herbs seem to rise from her body. 'She said also I must always be near you when you need me.'

I said nothing. A hawk rose suddenly in the sky, a dark arrow shot from the earth that seemed suddenly to change course, to hang in the air and to plunge again to the impenetrable barrier of shrubs moving in a dark tide to the great rock where the goat was sacrificed at the Feast of Dionysius. 'That is what we must beware of,' she said.

'I don't understand.'

'We prey on each other. Animals and men live off each other. Men often call it love. You must always be free to leave me.' She swung round suddenly. Her blue eyes had deepened, the blue of the seas darkened and mysterious and frightening at twilight. 'Do you think I love you?' she added.

'I have never thought about it. I have only just met you.'

'Only met me.' She looked at me with a sudden, uncomprehending sadness and her cheeks were pale. 'And you really believe you have only met me?'

'No,' I lied. 'I remember something way back in childhood. Why do you ask me?'

'It doesn't matter.'

I took her hand. 'It must matter because we are lying here without explaining ourselves and I seemed to have known you always.'

Now she lay on her back with the spray of mint held to her nostrils and looked at the sky, blue at its zenith but silvered with the morning. I looked at her profile, the infinite gentleness of which was moulded by her soft mouth, at the unlined serenity of the flesh below her eyes. Her small breasts were pointed to the sky. Her body was absolutely still and she seemed not desiring but already satisfied. 'Would you come away with me if it were necessary?' she said.

'How long and how far?'

Her laughter was gentle and not at all chiding. 'I must wait,' she said. 'One day we will go away together. I will go when you ask me.'

'Where?'

'To Greece, to Eleusis.'

'Personides on the hill has been to Eleusis.'

'He is no better for it. You must go to Eleusis.'

'Why?'

'To be better for it.'

'Is it there we learn the mysteries that follow death?'

'No,' said a voice, 'The mystery that life is.'

The voice was so changed that I sat up abruptly. Before, when she had spoken, her voice was silvery and light and in another would have been described as mocking except for the compassion in her eyes and the expression of her mouth which seemed to say that I was a child, that she loved me dearly and could not understand why I stayed a child. But now her voice was deep throated and vibrating. Its resonance seemed to float around and away from us and to merge with the vibrating heat haze reflected already from the leaves of the myrtle. I thought that someone else had come up from behind us and she had been taken over by a spirit. 'Your voice is changed,' I cried.

'Has it?' Her voice had again the silvery intonation of falling water. 'I expect it was my mother.'

'How can she speak through you?'

'My mother is dead.'

'Ah,' I said. I understood that better because I knew that the dead

wander in the shades, seeking direction for themselves and sometimes giving it to others. 'Is your mother happy?'

'She is concerned for me but without sorrow. She comes to me
many nights according to the season and to what I need. When she
does not come I feel empty and abandoned but often she reminds me
of her presence by the perfume of verbena. When I was a child we
plucked and dried it together. It is my mother who says we must go
to Eleusis.'

'You with me? She doesn't know me.'

'She knows you rather better than you know yourself. She says
that when you lose consciousness of this world, when your father
thinks you are ill or a son of the Gods, that you have retreated to
other worlds, sometimes past and sometimes present. She says that
you are not as the majority and that it is necessary for your
knowledge of yourself to go to Eleusis.'

'Did she say for my happiness?' I had heard of these voices, living
and dead, which promise the earth and power or money but
principally power for those able to hear and profit by the voices.

'She said for your knowledge of yourself.'

'What is the good of knowing oneself? The philosphers talk about
it continually and it seems to me without reason. My father speaks of
it constantly. He himself is consistently without meaning.'

'The idea is to know really what you are intended to do.'

'Isn't that a matter of will?'

'No,' she said. 'My mother says will is evil and that the furies are
impregnated with it.'

'Did your mother say you must go with me?'

'Yes.'

'She is a strange mother.'

'She was an exceptional mother and I loved her.'

'And your father?'

'My father died years before my mother and it was during her
sorrow for him that she learnt to speak with the Gods. She is a
messenger between them and us. That is why you and I will never
see Artemis again, except perhaps when we die. I have no need to see
her because I have my mother. You will be guided too.'

'By whom?' I said.

She swung round on her face and watched intensely the pur-
poseful movement of a tiny beetle ascending a blade of grass. 'We

must wait and see. Perhaps someone, perhaps no one. This beetle does not know what it will meet at the end of the stalk.'

'Who takes care of you?' I said.

'A woman who was a slave and with slaves below her.'

'Are you lonely?' I said.

'Lonely?' I am living. Every second is teeming with life. I am not lonely but I have a great deal of solitude. There is nothing to stop us going to Eleusis.'

'My father,' I said.

'Your father will be no trouble at all.'

'How can you tell when you have never met him?'

'My mother says he is as weak as water.'

'I can't see him saying yes to our going to Eleusis.'

She knelt laughingly before me, once again with her hands upraised and her small breasts widening. 'Can you see him saying no to me?'

I could not understand her. It was as though she was saying that he would find her seductive. It did not matter if he did. Nothing fitted in with the blue, underwater glow of her eyes and the feeling that she was not only uncontaminated but untouchable. It was all very well her speaking of her mother. It seemed that the latter was exceeding her responsibilities in suggesting that her daughter should see my father. It was plain to me as daylight that this was what had happened and I did not like it. I was prepared for the human frailties of my father's Gods and Goddesses because I did not believe in their divinity. They were as restless as ourselves otherwise they would not be hovering about an unspecified kingdom between their world and ours. I believed in my own Gods and Goddesses because I had seen Artemis and she had led me unerringly to the girl who came over the hilltop that April morning with the land wind dying and the sea foam curling in the morning sun. I believed also in the messengers of Artemis whom I had seen and whom I had felt with my hands as a tingling zone of etherealized matter. But for a mother released by death from her earthly responsibilities to encourage her daughter to influence a weak man to part with his son seemed more than one expected of the dead. In a word it seemed hardly decent. 'I had rather you didn't see my father.'

'All right, we will wait,' she said.

We stayed until noon on the high hill and time between us was dead. I do not know what we spoke of from that moment, or if we spoke at all, but I know that with the sun at its meridian she rose quickly from the ground and gave me the mint she had held in her fingers. I did not know what to do with it because it was half crushed and seemed to be worthless. I did not treasure what she gave me because though she was beautiful and mysterious and clearly sent to me it was all so impersonal and without desire that I seemed to be drifting on a cloud. But I took the mint and as I did so she said, 'All that lives is precious. Give it life a little longer.'

'Why is all that lives precious? You say this of a viper or a fox?'

'Because one day all beings die and learn in dying. I am going now.' She rose suddenly. She turned and faced me for a second. Slowly and deliberately she looked downwards at her breasts. As she did so they seemed to rise and tighten and asked to be caressed. Then she raised her eyes from her breasts and looked at me solemnly, intently. If all the Gods had asked me what I saw in her eyes I would have said an inviolable chastity. 'I will see you soon,' she added quickly.

'When?'

'Soon.'

Suddenly, stupidly I said, 'I love you.'

'Soon,' she said coolly. She smiled so serenely that her indifference to what I said seemed insensitive and cruel.

'You cannot go like that.'

'Very soon,' she said. 'And, oh, my name is Daria.'

I lived the next day in a haze of feeling. When my father spoke I did not answer. The meaning of his words seemed to trail like a cloud of vapour many minutes after their utterance. Nevertheless, through the haze, what I saw was sharp and illumined. There was the first wild rose, thin petalled, translucent, shining and pallid against the darkness of its leaves which had withstood the winter. There was an opal green flush in the sky at twilight and, farther to sea, the purple menace of low clouds over Crete.

I came out of this clouded world late in the evening. I asked my father about Eleusis. There was nobody else to ask except the wise man Personides and it was too late to consult him. Nor did I like him because of his cruelty to my father in rejecting so precipitately the latter's contention that I was a son of the Gods. As a matter of fact it was a lucky chance. My father was flattered that I consulted him and the theme of Eleusis was ideally suited to his genius for turning the nebulous into the concrete and utilizing it to his own advantage. 'Eleusis is the centre of the great Mysteries. Everybody should go there.'

'Have you been?' I said.

'It is a long way and I have already learnt much. A younger man——'

'I could go for you,' I said suddenly. I was aware that this conversation had been taken out of my hands. Someone was speaking for me and when I listened to my voice it was musical, authoritative and not my own.

My father was highly gratified. Like all failed prophets it made him drunk to acquire even one convert. 'One day, perhaps. Now what can I tell you?'

'All you know,' I said.

'Eleusis offers the absolute proof of the reality of the Gods. Those worthy of the experience are enabled to talk to them and be reassured of their existence. They learn also that we as well as the Gods are immortal, provided of course we do the will of the Gods.'

'And all this can be compressed into a short pilgrimage?'

'So I understand. I regret that I have never been able to make it.' I could not remember a time when he had not been free to go anywhere. 'Of course I have meditated a good deal of my life.' My father looked at the ceiling and was obviously trying to convey that he himself was above and beyond Eleusis which was undeniably useful to those who had little faith.

'I would like to go,' I said.

'I'd like you to go,' he added graciously. 'When you are a little older.'

That night the moon was young, a thin crescent chalky and lightless against the liquid glitter of great stars low in the sky. I went out alone because all of a sudden it had become unbearably necessary to think of the girl on the hill. I went to the low grove in the windless hollow to the right of the house. Even in the heat of the sun it was dappled with the shadows of the pines but now, overhung only by the stars which seemed suspended from invisible branches, it was dark and silent. It was seething with some kind of shadowy half life and I wondered if serpents were abroad in its recesses. I walked through its shadows and the beams of improbable starlight inserted

28

between the trunks of the sea pines. The air was quivering with menace and I wondered if we would suffer one of those tremblings of the earth which brought down houses on Crete but which here did no more than shake the island like a boat caught in the swell around the southern point.

I saw the white figure flitting between the trees at the edge of the forest. I thought at first it was a cloud of moths loose between the trees, their wings glistening with starlight, in the luminous half light which came from the sea on summer nights. Then I saw it was Thekla. I called her to me. 'What are you doing?'

'I was looking at the moon.' About her face was a great innocence and I knew that her lies were automatic, without significance and did not arise in her soul.

'There is very little moon to look at.'

'I was looking for you.'

I looked at her broad shining face and frank eyes and saw that what in her mother was possessive and bestial was in her merely frank and a kind of generosity. I took her in my arms. I drew her into the shadow of the trees. Her body was cool and thrilling as it tightened a little with the clasp of my hands. She wore a tunic skirt hung from the shoulders and her breasts were covered but under the soft woven wool I could feel them rising towards me and hard and urgent. I thought she would be my first, that the night was still, and that the perfumes from the rosemary and thyme came even at night because of the drenching of the sun by day. I carried her towards a gap in the trees where the moss on the ground was livid and deep green because of the spring which bubbled out of the earth and spilled a million small crystals in the green absorbent cushions. I felt Daria beside me. I could not see her though her hands folded me from behind and I felt their impact. I felt thin rivulets of exhilarating coolness moulded to my body where her psyche touched me. I put my hands on hers but they had no substance, only the impact of her healing coolness. I could not see her but I heard her voice. She was speaking not in her own light, laughing accents but with the deep vibrating intonation she had used on the hill when her mother spoke through her. 'Not yet,' she said. 'Be tender and caress her but do not love her yet.'

Thekla sensed that I was held by something but was unaware of any presence. She had heard no voice. It was some time before I

29

knew that the voices of the spirits are audible only to a few and that most of the world is deaf when they talk. I have heard wise men argue that if a voice is not audible to all it is non-existent. This argument is full of the intricate madness which afflicts wise men. If a voice is unheard or only relatively audible this is because there are degrees of hearing. There are some who can hear the rustle of a glow-worm. There are others indifferent to the rumble of thunder. What Thekla perceived was directly from me. She felt that suddenly my attention was elsewhere. 'I am not good enough and you don't like me.'

'You are more than good enough. Of course I like you.'

'You don't like my body.' Her face was infinitely moving when she asked the questions. When women are born to poverty and servitude it adds to the value they place on their bodies. Perhaps they believe it is all they have.

'I love your body and one day it will be mine.'

'I wish I were a free woman and a lady.'

'Why?'

'Then I could ask you to promise to take me.'

'There is no need to promise. Let's go,' I said. I was surprised at the tenderness I felt towards her when my arms encircled her trunk and felt her breasts that were as tender and submissive as herself. I saw her to the door of her hut and went into the house to sleep.

4

NOW the heat of Summer was upon us. The hill before the house was afire with broom. It flowered in between the rocks overtopping the sea. With the sea wind blowing we saw not only its golden aura adrift in the air but felt its perfume blowing towards us from the hills and suspended in the hollow.

I had come up from the path running from the porch to the left of the house, the path which leads past the spring with the leaning fig tree bent at a sharp angle and the pocket of vines between the rocks which give shelter to the old oak's roots. There by the spring the forest was thickest. There were groves of arbutus with the sun between the tree trunks. In Autumn the trees were afire with crimson. They were half illumined now by the glow reflected from their tawny trunks with the flaked-off bark. Beyond the arbutus was the clear light and shadow of the sea pines with the soil sandy between the tree trunks. Farther away was the alien and silver mystery of the olive groves which shed the atmosphere of moonlight at the height of noon.

Growing by the dust of the path near the spring I found the first red rose. There were two kinds of rose in the island. One was pale pink with infinitely winding branches which kept its leaves green through the months of Winter. There was also the shorter shrub rose with its dark red petals and yellow stamens, the rose with the deep scent used by the doctors and makers of perfume. I found by the spring the first of the season. I plucked it and walked quickly up the path to the house. Daria was moving through the porch and followed by my father. The latter's face was in impossible disarray of obsequiousness and lust. There was reverence too mixed up with desire. His features looked less human than a hastily assembled map of the universe with the main features out of proportion and also out of position.

Daria walked towards me with the unmistakable long, swinging stride with which she first came over the hill and by which I will recognize her from all others throughout eternity. Her face broke into a smile like sunrise. Then she controlled herself deliberately. When she checked the fullness of her smile which was natural to her it was as though an accident had produced a wreckage of her features. When I held out the rose to her her face was still. I preferred its stillness to her half smile. I looked at her naked breasts intensely and deliberately because I felt this might emphasize the bond between us. Coolly, unblushingly, she looked away. This aching encounter was interrupted by my father. It was typical that he should make me happy by accident when I was most miserable. 'This lady will take you to Eleusis,' he said.

'Yes.'

'Is that all you can say? Surely some mark of gratitude, perhaps even an expression of joy——'

'I am very happy,' I said dully. I could not understand how or why Daria had come to the house and how she had won over my father. Then suddenly it came to me that whatever the mechanism it had been done and I would be alone for months with her. 'Very happy and very grateful,' I added like a priest repeating a boring incantation.

'Will you see me over the hill?' she said.

She kissed my father with a freedom which amazed me and which made him alarmingly young and because of which the lust flooded his features with a rush of blood and the reverence he had felt drowned in his engorged tissues. I was outside the proceedings and in no way disturbed. It was part of a plan in which my father pictured as a clown and was also the victim. Ultimately he had to be sacrificed and therefore merited a little consideration.

Going up the hill I came to life when I saw her feet bounding in unison with mine and felt the swing and vitality of her long striding thighs. 'Why did you go to my father?'

'My mother told me it was time.'

'Are the dead who speak always right?'

'Not always, but mostly for those they love.' ◄

'But how did you convince him?'

'He was convinced when I arrived. My mother spoke to him not in words but more deeply than thought. She spoke to him at such a deep level that he did not realize the thoughts which were being injected into his head.'

Just before she placed her foot on a flat pale stone I was struck by a dark thought. Had she used her mother to gain power over my father? It was for such reasons that I distrusted the Gods and their emissaries. I was different from most of the islanders in being deeply concerned with right and wrong. What they wanted was a traffic with the Gods which led almost to profit. They were little concerned with how the profit was acquired. There were ways you could get round the Gods. I find it hard to worship Gods who appear to be the dupes of man. I was thinking these thoughts when an adder slid across the pale stone and hissed with arched back as Daria's foot descended towards it. I pushed her aside and her foot fell elsewhere. 'Did you see the stripes on its back?' she said. 'White and black stripes mean good and evil.'

I felt she had read my thoughts. 'Was it right,' I said, 'for your mother to influence my father?'

'It is always wrong except for a good cause. It should only be done rarely.'

32

'What is a good cause?'

'Something that creates and does not involve exercising power over others.'

'Your mother exercised power over my father for a few minutes.'

'Only to make him do a single action. Not to lead him to lead a certain life. Only to do what he wanted to do. He always wanted you to go to Eleusis, to save him the necessity of going himself.'

'When do we go?'

'At the next full moon.'

5

BEFORE I went to Eleusis I said goodbye to my friends. I went to see Personides not because he was inspired but because he might help me. 'You will gain from the visit,' he said. 'After all, you are a son of the Gods.'

'But that is the direct opposite to what you said to my father. At least you might have let him be happy in his illusion.'

He looked at me intently. 'If you go to Eleusis you are not concerned with illusion. You go to discover the truth. When I say you are a son of the Gods it is because I believe you were conceived in a certain way.'

'What way?'

'Find out or don't. Surely you don't believe truth resides in another man's mouth.'

I looked at him intently. I had seen him differently to what I had seen him before. He revealed himself as different to the self he had shown to my father when I was younger. 'How do I find out?'

'Not by looking for your mother.'

'My mother is described as dead.'

'Call her dead,' he said. 'The dead speak sometimes but in a matter like this you will find nothing by direct asking of either the living or the dead.'

'And is to be a son of the Gods determined only by the planting of the seed? I don't believe it.'

'Nor I,' he said. 'It is only the part of a pattern. You have other signs.'

'Do you mean my absences, my straying out of time?'

'That and other things. You ask why too much.'

'I always understood that self knowledge was all.'

'So it is but you don't get it by asking.'

'How do you get it?'

'In different ways but always by living.'

'Have you been to Eleusis yourself?'

'Yes.'

'Were you initiated?'

'Yes, and don't ask me what I learnt.'

I was angered by his abruptness. 'Is a Mystery something holy because it is kept a mystery?'

'No, but while you keep asking such questions you are not fit to learn about the Mysteries. In them you see as you look at that cloud and know it to be a cloud. You learn from what you see, feel and hear and know to be true. You do not learn by reason. Reason is for barter and trade, for navigation, for the law makers and the worst kind of priests who see nothing and sell everything.'

'What in the name of Zeus is the point of my going to Eleusis?'

'Because you have come and asked me so many foolish questions you think clever.'

'Thank you,' I said. I thought with his keen eyes and sharp-edged features there was something unremitting and merciless about him.

'Always remember I am very fond of you.'

'Fond?' I found his words incredible.

He brushed my doubts aside with a sudden shattering, almost cataclysmic smile. It was as though his features had suddenly been struck by an earthquake. 'Come and see me when you return.'

I thanked him very much and went down the path.

On my way home it occurred to me that I had not seen Electra. She was two years older than me. When we were young we had played a great deal together. Now that we were older we had seen less of each other. This was certainly not Electra's doing. She was absolutely constant in that she never failed to tell me how much she loved me. She told me this in all manner of places, in her house, in mine and walking by the sea and sometimes in the forest in the silence and solitude of mid-afternoon. Yet never once had she

34

seemed open to the onslaughts of love. She wore her breasts covered which was rare for a girl of her position. Her father was a ship owner. She was well educated and could, and did, recite the poets for hours on end. I never truly understood what she meant when she said she loved me. She said what she loved was the soul in me but as I regarded the psyche as an influence directed on my ordinary self and the body it inhabited, it seemed that if she loved my soul she must love me as I was and that she most emphatically didn't. She had a habit of raising a subject in conversation and reminding me of it when we said farewell. Next time we met she would weave her way by serpentine, verbal felicities to what we had discussed at our last meeting and before I knew where I was she was asking me how much I had meditated on what she had told me before. Once, on a day in late Autumn, the sea lacerated by grey squalls and a high shrill wind, she clung to me with her thin, muscular, boy's arms and said she would love me always and that there was no way out. I hoped this was merely an effect of the setting, of the pale rock half blurred by the increasing sea mist, of the sodden turf darkened by the lightless moisture of a rotting walnut showing its dessicated and shrunken kernel, of the island going down to its death in Winter. I hoped that this was merely a passing Autumn in the heart because I could not face the prospect of a life commentating on the esoteric meanings in the poetry she read.

Today of all days I had to see her. I was going up the white path which leads to the long cliff to the south which receives the track from the outskirts of the port. My footsteps were stifled in the Summer dust. She was waiting where the two paths met. My first thought was that this was part of a pattern. Since I met Daria and had seen the huntress I was inclined to think of every incident in life as fitting closely into the next as in the model of a temple. I thought it would please Electra if I opened the conversation with this gambit. 'This was certainly planned,' I said. When I looked hard at Electra she appeared like a resigned but remorseless fate and I regretted my opening words as altogether too symbolical.

'It wasn't planned at all,' she said. 'You visited the wise man and came back here half casually because you remembered me in a pang of conscience. It's more than a half chance that you would have left the island without seeing me.'

'No, Electra, no.' I sat down beside her and took her hand. When she smiled she had the most beautiful smile in the world, more beautiful even than Daria. Her smile was beautiful because it happened very rarely and because it was a release for all the tensions within her. In it she escaped from herself, from her hard destiny to be a new kind of woman, made to sift and ponder and to fritter away in tense contemplation what she might have gained easily with a face and body like hers. For those of refined taste I suppose she was more beautiful than Daria. Her hair was blue-black and wavy, her forehead improbably pale and her eyes so black that it seemed sometimes that the pupils fused with the surrounding darkness. Her face was long oval and pale and her small features so perfect that there seemed almost an artistic unreality about them.

Her mouth was pitiful. Her red lips were soft and affectionate but there was always something imploring and anguished in their expression. You could say that she was more beautiful than Daria but she lacked the latter's total vitality. Daria gave me something mysterious and carried her physical self and human personality in the emanation which radiated from her. She came to me emitting an individual light and strengthened me by its radiance. There were times when Electra drained the life from me. It was paradoxical that Electra had the slim muscular legs and the easy shoulders of an athletic boy. She paid for the ease of her muscles with the tightening of her mind.

'Listen, Electra. I am going to Eleusis because lately I have been thinking a lot about these things. That is why I have seen so little of you. I have been thinking so hard.' Electra gave a half sniff, half sob which conveyed to me bitter disbelief and tragedy. I tried hard to disregard it but I still felt I had treated her badly. 'I believe that the fact that we are guided by the Gods and the messengers they send to us is only part of the story. I believe there is something bigger behind the Gods.'

'What is it?' said Electra. She had lost her sense of grievance and was all eagerness. I had made exactly the right remark. She had a fervid curiosity about everything in the world and still more about things out of and beyond it.

'I don't know,' I said. 'It is something nameless. When I come back I will tell you.'

'Will you come back?'

'I swear it.'

'By what?'

This was a difficult question in view of the imprecise state of my beliefs and my attenuated and torpid faith. 'On all you and I truly believe in,' I said in a fit of inspiration. I had the feeling all the time that somebody more gifted than myself was doing the talking for me. I was not quick-witted in conversation. I could pick up the atmosphere, another's joy or unhappiness with lightning speed. I could make jokes in company provided I was given time and there was no opposition, but essentially I was not quick-witted. But today the right words shuttled in and out of my brain quickly and precisely. They were accompanied by a curious lightness, a feeling of vibration in the air and a deep needling sensation with penetrating heat low down in my abdomen. This disquieted me as I wondered if it had anything to do with my illness.

Electra asked, 'What else will you try to find out at Eleusis?'

'What happens when we die.'

'Yes, yes.' Now she was all eagerness. Her eyes were darker than ever with her pupils widening. 'There is something more. It is not just waiting by the river to walk through Hades until we are called by the Gods.'

'Why do you think that?' I said. Now I was not just making conversation but aroused by her.

'Because nature does not work like that,' she said. 'Our souls cannot jump about like grasshoppers. The jump from earth to Heaven through Hades is too quick. I believe it is more gradual and there is a lot of learning. It seems to me right and sensible that there should be a lot of learning.'

'Well of course you've thought that all your life, haven't you?' I said. 'In all the poetry you read me you were always looking for what you thought the deeper meanings.'

'There *were* deeper meanings.' She gave an arrogant toss of her dark head and suddenly her eyes moistened and she added softly, 'So you remember the poetry I taught you.'

'Of course I remember.' I quoted the lines about how the song of the birds provoked the return of Orpheus. 'The God returns in the flight of the lark and his message is in its song.'

'But I never could have thought you would ever remember.'

'You were two years older and you were entitled to play at being my mother.'

'I pitied you because you had no mother. Then——' She looked away to the sea in its green mood with a sudden wind and the waves leaping in agitated pyramids.

I knew what I was expected to say. 'And I loved you too. You were the first being I ever loved and it still goes on.' My voice trailed off hopelessly. Then suddenly I felt the deep needling sensation low in my abdomen and with it the scent of broom. I looked round from where we were sitting. There was no broom on the headland. We had the world to ourselves. The headland was empty, the village was distant, there were no ships crossing the sea. We were alone in the world with the immense and expanding sorrow of the pain beginning in our hearts and disseminated through the world because we were not happy in the love that should have been between us. Then I heard a voice, not spoken, but a voice deeper than the deepest intuition because it expressed itself in words. The voice was Daria's. 'Tell her you were with her in the beginning and she will be nearest to you at the end.' Ever after that, when Daria was separated from me and had something to tell me, I felt the drifting sweetness of the broom and the prickling of pine needles low in my abdomen.

I put my arm around Electra. 'You were with me in the beginning. You will be nearest me at the end.'

She leaned her head against my shoulder. Suddenly she sobbed. I had never seen her cry before. As she wept the movements of her shoulders were tempestuous and the tears fell down. Then suddenly she smiled and for that moment in the darkness of her eyes there seemed a deeper mystery than in the eyes of Daria. I was not to know that the mystery came from a deeper deprivation and a greater sorrow. 'I know that in some way you love me,' she said. I held her hands more tightly. 'And I love you in every kind of way. I still play at being your mother.'

I looked down at the clean sharp lines of her muscular arms. It was difficult to think of her as a mother but she was everything when I looked at her face and saw the smouldering lava of her dark eyes with the flame not yet come to the surface.

She looked at me intently. 'I will think of you every day on rising and again at noon and lying down at night.' She got up suddenly. 'I ought to go now.' She drew me towards her. I felt her arms binding me in the cords of her hard, unyielding muscles. Then she went off with her springing boy's stride. Her head was slumped between her shoulders and I knew she was weeping.

She looked round at the turn of the path. She waved her hand briefly and fiercely. Her twisted smile was lit with the radiance of great courage. I knew that she would love me always and that part of my heart was hers forever. By the time I had reached the hollow I had no room in my mind for anyone but Daria. The sun was up and the wide sky cloudless. Daria was a creation of the light and the present. Electra was the moon and darkness and the future. I feared that Electra could wait.

6

LOOKING back on our journey to Eleusis I see it in blue and gold. It was not always like that. There were grey days and drizzle but all that was lightless dissolves in memory as the mist at dawn and I see us in Greece not yet near Eleusis and with the road still empty, our feet throwing up the dust of summer, the white on Daria's feet where her skin was protected by her sandals, her long free strides and always the light, thinly diffused from her hair but intense and unwavering from her deeply glowing eyes. Looking back in memory the blue is the blue of the sky but the gold is more a symbol woven of disparate threads, Daria's hair, the broom on the hills, the mid-Summer ardour of the midday sun because with the coming of Summer the whiteness went out from the light and the sky at noon was molten and burning. But I think truly the gold I see is the remains of a process of alchemy inside my brain. I had come from the silver of my home and morning across the silver of the sea. When I walked through the groves of olives, they, too, were rustling and silver in the winds of morning, but within my brain I was moving to another plane of being, stimulated by the outside colours but not dependent on them, and the light of this plane was undeviatingly gold. So, while I passed between the trunks of the olives, opaque and black with the leaves whirling in a silver cloud about them, or moved between the vines, their leaves powdered and silvered with the dust of Summer, I was also moving in an inner golden twilight, unlit by the remorseless sun.

All our journey, by day and night, I was enveloped by love. I do not ask this to be believed or understood because in this world there is always the light and the dark, and even if there is no hate and no dissension there are moods in the day when a cloud passes over the climate of the heart so that what is hopeful on waking becomes ominous at dusk. But, sleeping or awake, I cannot recall a moment of tension between us or a second when I did not feel myself engulfed by her love. Equally I cannot remember a single reference to what she felt for me. She took off her tunic at night and lay naked beside me. There was no constraint in her body and it was as though a sculptor had moulded us together in an unbroken unity. But before we slept she never uttered a word of love but would enquire whether the cloak she had folded for me was easy for my head and whether I needed more cover for my body.

Now that we were together I never saw into the future or the past. She never spoke at night with her dead mother or felt her presence by day. We lived perfectly in an instant and knife-edge present. We did not know that this was the peak of our existence, that we had already gained the summit and that the far slopes led undeviatingly downwards. We did not know then, what we would learn much later, that in those days we were looking at the unflawed crystal of our happiness. It seems to me that there is no sadness greater than that we do not know, while one is living it, the moment of our supreme happiness.

When we came nearer Eleusis there was a thickening of people on the roads. Some were simple peasants in rough tunics but most were richly dressed and many were riding in chariots. I was not troubled by what I saw but for the first time Daria's eyes were clouded. 'They come to buy wisdom,' she said.

'You can't tell that from their clothes.'

'You can from their eyes.'

That night she looked into the purse she carried on a belt round her waist next to her skin. She counted the emeralds she carried with her. They had belonged to her mother and she had taken them with her to pay the costs of our journey. My own contribution was less because my father counted his advice and the imperious unrolling of his wisdom as worth more than rubies.

We first came to Eleusis in the early morning. Before we reached the cave there were a few booths selling food and drink. I was disappointed because I expected something remote like the cave in our island where the oracle had lived for a short time. Daria consoled me. However much she lived in other worlds she could always see life as it was with unhesitatingly clarity. 'If they come from the ends of the earth they need food and drink. Why shouldn't it be near the temple? Do you want them to arrive exhausted?'

After the booths there was a colonnade of light pillars leading up to the cave. Before the cave was a semi-circular table with three men and one woman sitting round it. The men and woman were dressed in light blue robes. Daria took my hand very gently. She stroked my fingers one by one as though she were telling bad news to a sick child. 'We have come too late but we will learn much.'

'Why too late?'

'We were born too late. It was better here before we were born. There is no tragedy, my love.'

It was the first time she had called me my love but in that moment of foreboding I let it pass unnoticed. 'Come,' she said briskly, 'we have much to learn.'

'Why have we come too late?' I insisted.

'Because there are male priests. I always thought they were women.'

There was a priest who singled us out and beckoned us towards him. He was long faced and exceptionally smooth cheeked. It was difficult to tell his age. He cannot have been more than middle aged but looked younger. His skin had a kind of unhealthy grey opalescence. It was as though there was something ethereal about him but that what was etheric was tarnished. He had colourless, greyish, unsatiably seeing eyes with enormous pupils. While he beckoned us both towards him he had eyes only for Daria but when he looked at me his smile was fuller and caressing. It was as if he were willing to share a secret with me and that the secret concerned Daria.

He spoke almost exclusively to her. 'Have you come seeking initiation or merely a blessing and some knowledge?'

'For a little knowledge,' said Daria. Her smile was dazzling, artificial and I knew that there was no sincerity or illumination in it. Her eyes were intensely watchful.

41

'That can be given quickly,' said the priest. 'Initiation is only possible to a few and takes years.'

'I am sure we would not qualify.'

'You speak for the young man as well as yourself.'

'Yes, yes,' she said firmly and I knew that her mind was made up, that she regarded him as evil or stupid and that our journey was probably in vain.

The priest smiled. 'The most enlightened are often the most humble.'

'I don't think I am either,' said Daria.

All the time my attention was divided. I was sitting on the right of Daria with the translucent-faced priest directly in front of me. At his right was a dark-faced, sallow-skinned woman with a long head, a hawk nose, unblinking dark eyes and an imperious, half-disdainful mouth. I could see from the poise of her trunk and the set of her shoulders that she was tall. She smiled little. In repose her face was hard but when she looked at us her mouth relaxed to a tiny degree but sufficient to transform the expression of her face to one of watchful pity in which she knew all about us and condemned nothing. From the very beginning I felt that there was nothing I could hide from this woman. I was in her power and I could only hope her power was beneficent.

All the conversation was between the priest and Daria but I was aware of the priestess' glance as a kind of crossfire directed at me. I had the idea that she was warning me of something and knew that I did not realize the nature of the menace. I could not watch the priestess' face because all the time I was concentrating on the man and listening hard to what he was saying.

'Sometimes initiation is shorter than you think,' he said. Daria did not answer. 'There are special cases. Sometimes we encounter people who are almost born initiated. One can tell them at sight.'

'How? By marks on the body?' Daria's glance was direct and concentrated. I knew that she was not given to reason and sustained thinking. I knew also that now she was thinking hard.

'No. That is a rare and unimportant detail. It is a matter of emanation. We are trained to perceive emanations.'

The hawk-faced priestess on his right sat up stiffly and suddenly. I could almost feel the tension in her shoulders.

42

'Does the training take long?' said Daria.

'Years, years,' he said. 'And many are rejected.'

Daria laughed her silvery but deep echoing laughter. 'It is as well that I did not mean to be an initiate.'

'With you it will be only months.'

I was conscious of a great tension in the atmosphere. I felt that the little world round us, the people at the table, the cave behind, the light palpitating in white sheets in the sun of morning, would snap any minute and that after the cataclysm Daria would be taken from me. 'Perhaps you could tell me more,' she said. She had lost all her colour and her eyes were looking at him with such intensity that his own wavered. He looked deprecatingly in my direction. It was clear that my company was superfluous. I got up to go. This was a battle Daria had to fight out for herself and I believed she was capable of doing so. I had also an insatiable curiosity as to what he proposed for her. We had, after all, intended to learn all we could about the Mysteries.

Daria and the priest walked away not into the cave but by the path to its right. The country was flat and cornland and looked towards the sea. I rose from my seat. I looked at the hawk-nosed priestess but she made no attempt to detain me. I walked back down the colonnade and past a procession led by a youth reeking of scent, with heavily pomaded hair, with a white tunic edged with gold leaf and with pointed slippers of beaten gold. His cloak was extended in a train and two simpering creatures with short white tunics and a band of gold leaf around their hair were following him with the servile and allusive smiles of creatures born men but prepared to sell themselves as women. Behind these two sexless performers was a string of concubines with reddened lips and with vine leaves in their hair. I enquired from a bystander who was the leader of this menagerie. He told me that he was a prince, that his name was Antonides and that this was an inconsiderable proportion of his retinue. 'What is *he* doing here?'

'But it is obvious,' said the stranger, 'he has come to be initiated.'

'But to be initiated you have to see into the past and the future. This man cannot see farther than his next catamite.'

'He is a prince,' the stranger said briefly. He was obviously not a type to involve himself in theological argument.

I turned round and walked back through the colonnade towards the table. The hawk-faced woman was walking towards me. 'You wish to talk with me?' she said.

'I did not say so.'

'Nevertheless you wish to talk to me.'

'More than you can think,' I said.

'Not so much as I can feel. Let us go away from here. I do not wish to be seen.' We turned down a small path that curved round a rock cleft in the middle, with the cleft not looking towards the colonnade and with a flat boulder where two people could sit. 'I don't wish to leave Daria too long,' I said.

'She will come to no harm. What do you fear for her?'

'It is for you to tell me,' I said.

'No, never. Fear is always individual to him who fears. Tell me what you think is happening.'

'I cannot think. It is for you to tell me.'

'Give me one of the rubies you carry in your purse.' I did as she told me. Normally I would have been wary of falling into the hands of a fraudulent soothsayer but all of a sudden I was overcome with an irresistible desire to speak my heart to her. I knew suddenly that she and not Eleusis itself was what I had come for. I knew that what happened between Daria and the priest was secondary. I treated Daria almost as a messenger of the Gods, but now I knew I was here in my own right and I sat down with the priestess while she held the ruby in one hand and my own wrist in the other. 'Now tell me what you see,' she said.

'I see the corn and a dove and the blue of the sea.'

'It is seen with your senses. What else do you see?'

'What I imagine——'

'What you are seeing is not imagination. What do you mean when you say that you see with your mind's eye?'

'That I have remembered something I have liked.'

'But now you are seeing something you don't like. What is it you are seeing?'

'Nothing.'

'Tell the truth.'

'I cannot tell you what degrades me and what makes me feel childish.'

'Nevertheless tell me,' she said.

'I see Daria lying naked on a couch. A man is bending over

her. I see the painted creature I saw in the colonnade.'

'No, no. The last sentence is foolish. It is imagination born of your own fear. Simply go on seeing. Seeing with your mind's eye is an inner seeing without using your senses. You have it after and sometimes before your attacks of unconsciousness. Now you have it with my holding your hand. I am taking one part of your consciousness away from you. You are afraid because after you saw her with a man bending over her you hurried back terrified to ordinary consciousness because of your fear of the human doll you saw in the colonnade.'

'Yes, yes. I am back with her. She seems still naked and with a man bending over her. It is not the painted puppet I saw just now. Now this other man is making love to her. I don't understand, she is not resisting. It is in a way unendurable yet I endure it.'

'I am holding your hand.'

'I think I have seen enough,' I said. 'Is that one of the Eleusian Mysteries? I am bewildered.'

'My poor child.'

In spite of her harsh profile and strong, angular body I was oddly moved when she said 'My poor child'. It was inexplicable that I felt protected, secure and in some odd way inviolable while I was with her. 'So I have wasted my time.'

'Wasted? What you will see here will be more important than anything which has happened before.'

'And to Daria too?'

'Yes, also to Daria. We must go back now. Don't ask any questions in front of the priest.'

'I am troubled,' I said. 'How can I have confidence in people who claim to be in contact with the Gods and who are divided amongst themselves.'

'How indeed?' she said. 'It is what I will explain. Come back here tonight after dark and bring the girl with you.'

When we were close to the cave Daria came round the corner with the priest. Her hair was so glistening that its fine spun gold seemed to float above her forehead. Her eyes were glowing with love and her mouth was widened to its full extent in the welcome she gave me. She disregarded the priest and the priestess. 'Do you know that's the longest time we have been separated for months? It was like being dead.' She was oblivious to the world, to the priests and priestesses and living only in the immediacy of a desire to be with me. For some odd reason I forebore to call it love.

That afternoon we went away from the world in a country of vineyards with a single spring. We sat near the spring with its diamond clear water tasting, in the burning plain, of inaccessible heights and with the dappled shadows of a fig tree leaning uncertainly over us and darkening and lightening, in alternate movements, the glitter of Daria's hair. 'The priest was evil,' I said.

'Oh yes,' she said coolly.

'It doesn't worry you to be in contact with evil?'

'Very little. I am sickened by it and throw it off quickly.'

'But isn't it heart-breaking to you that we came these many miles to find something we venerated and for which we hoped so much and to find it infiltrated with evil?'

'No, why?' she said. She picked a vine leaf. She put it in her mouth and chewed it reflectively. 'Isn't that a tribute to Eleusis?' Doesn't great good always attract great evil? Isn't there a black entity near every sacred spring? If you wish to be healed at a well don't you pass first through a zone where your pains are worse?'

'What was it he wished of you?'

'What he wished was reasonable enough. He said I was a creature of the body and the psyche. The spirit would grow later but not in this life. He said that some can only achieve oneness and loss of their own identity by physical love. He said that this was a common experience between lovers. When they lay together was the only time in their lives they could abandon themselves.'

'How horrible that he said all this to you.'

'But surely what he said was reasonable.'

'It shocks me to hear you,' I said. This was the first time in our lives that there was any pain and separation between us.

'Then he told me that I was one of those with a limited capacity to act as a messenger of the Gods. Such people, if they are ardent physically, are able to wake in others still less developed a feeling of unity with life and the Gods.'

'By making love?'

'Yes.'

'With just anyone?' I said.

'With someone selected by the priest. Someone likely to benefit from him.'

'What did you say?'

'I would think it over.'

'You horrify me.'

Every vestige of colour went from her face and her eyes were lightless. 'That I should ever have heard you say that.'

'Can't you understand that anyone loving you as I do——?'

I stopped suddenly. I had never used the word love and I waited to see its effect on her. She accepted what I said without the smallest change of expression. 'What difference does that make?' she said. 'We came to listen to what we could hear. We can but listen to what is told us freely. I have no desire to ask a lot of questions. I am not like your friend Electra.' She mentioned Electra completely without bitterness. 'But surely it would be foolish to stop our ears to what they tell us?'

'It is what they are asking you to do that counts.'

'Is it inevitable that I do what anyone asks me? Did you know I am a virgin?'

'Yes.'

'We will go back and see the woman priestess tonight.'

That day there was a brief and piercing twilight and after it was over the stars were low and reflected in the sea. There were a few people walking the long colonnade to the cave. These were mostly grave-faced people of ripe age and soberly dressed. Some looked wise and some merely miserable. They were a world different from the dilapidated exquisite who had pranced between the columns that morning. I was reassured by the smaller number of people and by their gravity. We crossed between the columns and walked down the path to the fissured rock. The priestess was sitting there waiting for us on the block of stone and it seemed as though she had been there through all eternity. 'Sit one on each side,' she said. 'Each give me a hand.'

We sat silently for a time. The scent of rosemary was sharper than incense with the fall of night and the coming of the sea wind. She turned to Daria. 'Ask me what you want to know.'

'No,' said Daria. 'You are very kind but I will ask nothing. I am happy and free. I wish for him to be the same.' Daria put her hand on my shoulder. 'While you talk I will walk by the sea.'

I cried to her to stay but she rose smiling and went from us. I followed her going until her white tunic was the colour and texture of a night flying moth and there seemed to be no body inside it.

'Some curse has come upon us,' I cried. 'We will go back home. We will go tomorrow.'

'Not tomorrow,' said the priestess. 'Daria is wise. She is wise to leave you with me. Also she is doing this for your sake.'

'It cannot be that I am more capable of learning than she is.'

The priestess laughed softly. 'No, certainly, you are not more developed. There are other reasons.'

'I must know,' I said.

'You will know one day. It is not for me to tell you.'

'What can you tell me?'

'You have let go my hand. Now hold it again.'

'Do I need the ruby?'

Her laughter was so frank and human that it was difficult to feel any deep veneration for her. In any case what I had seen already of Eleusis had taken away my reverence for it. 'The ruby was not necessary,' she said. 'I only asked you to hold it because I knew your faith would be still less if you only held my hand. Even then, when you did so, you saw what you saw and are still wounded by it. What do you see now?'

'I don't wish to tell you.'

'Then wait until you do. Remember always it is not necessary to tell me anything. Everything in life is known but knowing is not necessarily derived from telling.'

All of a sudden my timidity and squeamishness were gone. I would have spoken of what I had seen with young men or girls but I felt that such matters were defiling for a priestess. But I could not think of the woman beside me in that role because she seemed so near to me and so human and unsanctified. She only looked like a priestess when I saw her fine-cut prophetic profile, sharp, pale and stony with the starlight behind it. 'I see young girls dragged into a dark forest. I see men drunken and draped in vine leaves. What I see is like what happens at the Spring festivals. It is the same only more vivid and wait, wait, one girl is Daria. They are dragging her away. I hear their cries and laughter. Do I go on seeing?

'Why not? Who is being hurt?'

'I am.'

'We must all bear our own wounds and there is nothing in the whole pattern of destiny we can do to avoid it. Remember to accept your pains. But go on watching.'

What I saw was the first scene but played more slowly. The girls were led and not dragged into the forest. The men were drunk and grinning but their movements were less violent and the vine leaves tangled in their hair were arranged in some kind of order. Then I saw Daria. She was naked in a clearing in the forest. She lay on the grass and the men with the engorged faces and the straying vine leaves were gathered in a circle about her. Her eyes were still and unafraid. They were looking at something beyond the circle of grinning faces. Then, very slowly, she covered her breast with her hands. As she did so I heard, drifting between the branches of the grove, a mist of music, half sound, half odour. Amidst the notes of a flute were mixed, in an unearthly compound of sensations, the wind in the trees and the memories of all the waves which since time began had beaten in vain on the shore. Then I saw rising from among them but somehow also overtopping the shrubs, the figure of the male God with the serene face and the undemanding, persuasive smile. He raised his lute and played a yearning music which pointed to some fulfilment of life beyond anything possible to the human satyrs and even to Daria who lay naked on her bed of moss waiting for them. Then the music descended from its half cry of longing and the notes declined softly like falling water. Daria rose naked from the floor of the forest. The men around her removed the vine leaves from their hair. They stood aside as she walked towards them. She kissed each on the forehead and went through the forest to where the land rose gently to another clearing singing with the spring and with the moon upon it. She splashed her body with the water at the spring and walked under the moon with what seemed like a shower of diamonds descending from her.

'What have you seen?' said the priestess.

I told her all I had seen and she asked me to interpret it. I said this was impossible for me, that this task was hers and that she was an oracle but she only pressed my wrist more tightly and, slowly at first but gaining in confidence I said, 'Now I know what I have seen. What I saw first was the Dionysian frenzies. It was for whole weeks in Spring and, as it is with us now for two or three nights when the moon is full, it is permissible for any man to take any woman who walks abroad at night. What I saw afterwards was Orpheus taming the frenzy with his music, keeping what was good in the desire and in the beauty of Daria's body seen in the moonlight. I see now that the Orphic Rites were arranged. The impulse was good. It was part of the Spring and the goodness of the earth which is always creative. What was good in a bursting bud, in a developing ear of wheat, was good in a man and a woman but there is no frenzy in the fertilization of plants. By his music Orpheus took the frenzy out of the Dionysian orgies. Under his influence the girls and the women were chosen. It was a kind of representative tableau of nature. Also it was not simply the lust of beast for beast. Each couple were attuned to each other not by passion and lust alone, but because they lived at the same rhythms and saw and felt things in the selfsame way so that, in the art of love, something of the oneness they had achieved persisted and the effect of their loving lasted through the heat of Summer until the Autumn came.'

'Tell me what happened to Orpheus,' she said.

'The ignorant believed that all the year round, he desired to deflower a number of their most beautiful girls. They did not understand that he believed he could train women to heal a great deal of sickness by the intimate gestures of physical love. The village women preferred that their daughters took their chances over a short season with the local drunkards.'

'You talk of Orpheus as though he was living and an ordinary human.'

'I do,' I said. 'Am I wrong?'

'Do you think you are wrong?' she said.

'No.'

'Yes, you are right. In the future you will find that you will only be wrong when you fail to follow your intuitions.'

'I remember arguing with my father that Apollo was a man built into a legend by the stories about him. I believed that Orpheus could communicate with animals as I can by whistling to dolphins. Also he could accommodate his music to the song of birds and the hiss of adders and could use it as a sedative for the frenzies of man.'

She spoke very slowly. 'So what we call Gods are only men deified in the minds of people after centuries?'

'They are heroes and exceptional men glorified by the memory of their abilities.' I paused and added, 'And of course they can come back to us.'

50

'But surely it is not only these so-called Gods who return to us. There are many who come back after death. Daria's mother talks constantly to her. Such women are sent by the Gods when the latter prefer not to come themselves.'

'I myself have seen Artemis.'

'Once,' she said. 'You will not see her again.' She paused and looked upward to the blue and trackless mysteries between the stars. 'Yes, I think once again.'

'When?'

She smiled. 'You only ask the where and when of false prophets.'

'Where does Daria enter into all this?'

'She enters now.' She stood up and called towards the shore.

I saw Daria, faint and evanescent, sometimes disappearing and sometimes materialized, as she moved towards us from the shore.

'Why did I see her naked in both the Dionysian and Orphic Rites? What do they want of her in Eleusis and how does this connect with what I saw in the earlier orgies?'

'Now there are no orgies. What they require of her is that she becomes a priestess and ministers to the sick and agonized with her body. She can take a bereaved husband in her arms and comfort him while he is still bewailing his wife. Is that worth doing?'

'Yes, provided it is not Daria who does it.'

'There are men able to obtain a glimpse of reality impossible for them except through a woman's body. One can in this way see visions of the future or fragments of the past piecing themselves together like the stones of a mosaic. In the Dionysian frenzies there were women who, annihilated by their own passion at the end of the night, would prophesy and live to see their prophesies fulfilled. Is this worth doing?'

'For some,' I said.

Now Daria was near us. Wisps of vapour moved over the stars in the highest vault of the sky. The moon was up and its light upon the waters. I saw the lines of her body against the light and through her light tunic and for the first time I desired her, hotly and possessively, and her eyes on mine were afire and deeper, glowing now with an impossible iridescence like the gentians on the hills. I was moving towards her with my arms outstretched when the voice of the priestess sounded clear and a little metallic behind me. 'Will you do what they want, my child?' she said.

'What would *you* do?' said Daria.

'That you can only answer yourself.'

'No,' she said.

'Why, why?' said the priestess. Her words were demanding but her voice very gentle. 'Some would say it was a great opportunity.'

'Because it is organized. It is organized by men. I will give myself but I will not be given. I will give myself one day but not in Eleusis.'

The priestess stooped towards her and kissed her forehead. 'You are of a certain kind. You have little to learn. You will rise to a certain level but not beyond it.'

We sat very quietly and in the stillness of the night the vapours from the dark shrubs came upwards towards us and I knew that the rosemary, the thyme and the wild daphne were plants that spoke to us not through the inconspicuous beauty of their flowers but through the scents that were, at this hour, evoked by the moon and not merely the perfumes of flowers but the aura of spirits which encircled us. I remembered how, when I was parted from Daria, I would feel the penetrating sweetness of the smell of broom and know her to be present when in her body she was at the other end of the island. All the messengers of the Gods seemed to clamour around us on that still night when the sea itself was silent, with its silence mingled with the unmoving air and the light of the moon was level and unwavering and even the starlight unflickering and constant. Suddenly I spoke aloud the thought that was welling up in my throat like a physical presence, like a voice within that had almost physical substance as though a prophet materialized in my flesh and I was struggling either to control or expel him. 'We did not come here to learn how much can be achieved by physical love. Why should we when both of us are virgins? We believe there are other mysteries. Certainly you have told us much and it is something to know that the Gods and Goddesses were men and women like ourselves who after death have either the power of returning to the world or of sending their messengers to speak with us. What else have you to tell us?'

'Nothing,' she said. 'But we will walk to the sea.'

She walked between us to the shore and while she did so she held one of our hands with each of her own. Walking towards the sea my head was light and I seemed to be floating on air. Then the tension of the air seemed to lift from the ground. It was as though I drifted through space a few inches from the earth and the priestess held my hand to prevent me fleeing to the sky. Of course I knew that no such supernatural happening had overtaken me because I know now that there is no such thing as the supernatural. There are things visible and invisible, palpable and impalpable, with one system of laws governing all. What was thought supernatural or miraculous was merely evidence that in this world there are items of knowledge we cannot acquire and that, until our blunt senses are freed by death, there are things we cannot learn. When, instead of being light, my head tightened and the tension gripped me by the throat, I knew that as well as a voice struggling to speak within me I was in the grip of my illness. Here, with the priestess, I knew that my malady, and the being with the prophetic voice rising like a serpent whose coils were entwined in my tissues, were one and the same.

At that moment the earth opened before me. I saw a huge, fanged cave like the mouth of an old lion and all the world outside it shuddered and shook itself clear of the rocks that bound it together and in that moment the whole world died. Then there was a moment after the death of the world when all was still. I, too, was still for, lying on the ground, I saw the end of the world and the stars above me. Between me and the stars were Daria and the priestess. Daria's tunic was transparent in the moonlight and I saw her body as if wrapped in gauze. I desired her now with a pain that impaled me. It pierced my flesh from low in my abdomen to my solar plexus. I could not see the priestess. I only felt her presence behind my shoulder. What was strange was that the priestess herself was also shimmering, translucent and without body. She was only a silver outline. There were no longer hawk-like lines to her face which was pitying and gentle and I did not see her features but only her smile. Then I saw Daria drawn into the cave by two long arms which were human but larger than human. I saw her look pityingly not at me but at the priestess. She widened her arms in the same gesture as I had seen when she came towards me over the hill for the first time. Then I heard myself shrieking and I heard also the priestess saying, 'That is the cry which precedes the convulsion,' and I knew that one of my moments of writhing darkness was descending on me and the world shut out.

When I came to I returned to a dark world where there was only the mouth of the cave and around it the wrecked earth without contours. The smooth, weather-worn rocks were buried beneath a sea of lava with the top layers blown off in a fog of powdered carbon. Daria was gone and I cried once again but this time thinly, out of the desolation of my heart and not with the stridor of my epileptic cry. Now I saw the priestess facing me, crouched on the ground, not with her hands wide-stretched in welcome like Daria's but infinitely void as though they had been emptied in a second of the whole harvest of life. 'She is gone,' she said. Then she leaned towards me. Her hands were swollen and deformed with the knotted joints of very old people. 'This is your hell and mine. It is the only way to traverse hell to know that you are locked within it. This is the hell of the demons, the invasion of the fringe of Hades where there are still green fields for the happy spirits but where the earth is invaded by those ascending from the caverns.'

I asked her with the inner voice still gripping my throat what had happened to me. The cave had opened with the tremor of the earth and after that there had been an earthquake and the sea had risen. The God of the underworld had ascended from the deepest of the tunnels because, with the earth opening the cave in the world's surface, he had seen the light at the far end of his steeply ascending tunnel. Daria had stood at the mouth of the cave. The priestess had called her back too late and Daria was withdrawn into the underworld of darkness.

'Will she stay there forever?' I said. 'To me we are in a world of demons without light. In the end are the Gods and Goddesses defeated?'

'Do you believe no longer in the Gods and Goddesses?'

'I believe in them and I believe them to be defeated. I believe that the forces of darkness are in the end triumphant. I know like you that night follows day.'

Then there was an indefinable time of agony, darkness and of headache and confusion. I could not tell, on looking at each facet of agony, what was the truth of life in the world and what was the throbbing insistence of my illness which left me always with a headache and the feeling of the world swaying and loose on its axis and threatened by a force greater than the combined efforts of all the Gods and Goddesses. Then I slipped into some lapse of time, into a darkness seething with what was indefinable, with gesticulating and largely idiot figures which pointed in different directions as though to confuse me as to the path I could take for my own liberation,

54

and others which were beautiful and still and which told me that all I could do was to rely on the inner core of stillness within myself. I concentrated on one of these figures and thought it Daria, but when I opened my eyes still further I found it was the priestess but changed from a lithe, dark woman with a hawk-like profile to a sadly smiling woman with dark gold hair, seated on a stone, her arms resting each side on stone supports and pointing past me to the mouth of the cave. I turned my head slowly. At first I thought that the glistening figure standing at the mouth of the cave was Artemis whom I had seen by the pool, but now I saw it was Daria as I had seen her in the Orphic vision when she had walked naked through the forest and washed off the memories of the lusts of man when the spring water poured off her body like a thousand diamonds.

The priestess sat on her stone chair in the middle of a land which was ruined in a sea of lava. There were no flowers and no vines and the ether round the world was clogged and airless. The earth was dead and nothing would grow on it. The priestess looked to the cave which was alive with a writhing, serpentine, hidden life of evil entities reaching upwards to impregnate the dead matter of the earth with their own vitality. Where Daria stood there was a film of light sometimes sucked into the cave by the magnetism of the evil within and sometimes billowing out to the world because of the yearning love in her for me and the flowers we had known in our own island.

'She is going now,' said the priestess. 'She will come back with the Spring.'

'No, I am going with her. It cannot be that I have seen her for the last time.'

'You cannot go with her because you are not a woman and the love in you is not passive. You are near to a woman but not near enough to lie fallow until the earth awakens. She will come back with the Spring.'

With a moan I saw Daria drawn back into the darkness of the cave. I do not know whether the moan was hers or mine or whether it was blended, not of our voices or our hearts but from the cry of a whole world, a kind of Autumn lament which was timeless as though the falling leaves of the world spoke through our bodies and the snow on the mountains fell within our hearts. Then while I lay on the ground the sky lightened a little. The spectral glow of a dead moon swept over the lava. It seemed that as well as the earth the moon and the planets were dead. All the time the priestess sat in the chair and while I lay on the ground I had an impression of coming back more to normal consciousness, of Daria being beside the priestess in the chair and at the same time being buried in the stifling tunnels of the earth below the lava.

Then, at first slowly, but later quite quickly, the light came back. It returned first to the sea with the moon reborn in the shallows by the shore. Then out to sea the dolphins returned and swam inshore with the sun come back. Then with the sun there were now fissures of gold and the black lava. The fissures were golden from the descending sun and from the ears of wheat showered between the lava by invisible hands. Then, with the first timorous shoots of wheat, the flowers came back. There was a flood of anemones blue in the shadows and red where they flowered in the full sunshine. Now the sun was full on the face of the priestess and the widening of her arms was despairing no more. There was love and hope in the width of her gesture. Once again the girl in the white tunic was at the mouth of the cave, shielding her eyes from the sun and with dark arms receding about her. This time the girl was not Daria. She walked across the flood of anemones, the first crocuses and the scented yellow jasmine, because in that Spring all the flowers came together after a long lapse of night. As well as the full Springtime was the white tornado of almond, spreading from the cave to the mountain with the sun on its slopes and the shadows blue in the hollows between the hills.

Daria knelt beside me. 'You are better now.'

The priestess knelt also and said, 'What have you seen?' In these two simple phrases was the whole difference between Daria and the priestess.

'I have seen something which was a lesson but I am too confused to read it.'

'Not just a lesson but history,' said the priestess. 'What is worth interpreting has always happened. What we call the Mysteries are made by men and time. Had you been here with Orpheus you would have seen that men were different in those days. They escaped from their flesh and lived more in a palpitating envelope in which they could communicate with each other without words and with animals without thoughts.'

'What I have seen is the story of Demeter.'

'Is it true?' she said. 'You yourself have said that the Mysteries are made by living people.'

'This is beyond me,' I answered. 'I cannot see that Pluto is anything but a creation of the mind. How could any man act so as to be a God of an underworld?'

The priestess smiled. 'We cannot imagine what has never happened. Imagination is the remembrance of forgotten experiences of ourselves and others.'

'But are there not rites to enable me to see? I have heard there are rooms with mirrors and alternating light and shadows and that men see the past and the future reflected in the mirrors.'

'There are such rooms and instruments but wherever men have recourse to instruments it is because they are impoverished. The instruments are a substitute for something interior which is lacking. You have no need of such artificial help because already you look backwards and forwards in what they call your malady in which you lose consciousness.'

'I only look forward,' I said.

'You have now moved backward in seeing Daria and Persephone at the mouth of the cave.'

'Why did I see them both?' I asked.

'When did you see Daria?'

'Towards the end, when I was becoming conscious.'

'And so?'

'I saw the Goddess when I was most out of time and had left this world behind me. Daria took her place when I was returning to this life. Daria has the gift of replacing the Goddesses when consciousness is half returned.'

'You learn rapidly,' said the priestess.

'There is a man who lives by the harbour in the island who would say that I saw Daria when I came back to life merely because I am in love with her and because when I was more confused she became for me Persephone, Artemis and other Goddesses in the pantheon.'

'How would he explain that she comes to you in the smell of broom, that you feel her hands upon you and that she talks to you when she is not present? But listen to the cynic. It is part of your apprenticeship. You must listen to reason to learn its limitations. The aim of reason is the abolition of the Gods and the deification of man, each man whatever his talents. You have to choose between seeing the Gods as once men, as in the mythologies concerning Orpheus and Apollo, or the making of each man to be a God and a lord over the earth. It is in this way that remote man destroyed himself in the past and will do so again.'

'When did he destroy himself?'

'It will be as you will see.'

I looked from the priestess to Daria and behind them both at the moon clear in the sky like an untarnished coin with no wisp of vapour trailing across it. I looked at the stars reflected melting in the sea in silver raindrops. I smelt all the scents of night clearly because the earth was hushed and there was no land breeze. It was a comfort to return to the earth tired and silent, to feel nothing but the world about me, the immortally murmuring sea, the flowers of the almonds suspended motionless in the night air as though the Gods themselves had ceased breathing. I thought no more of the personal significance of what I had seen, of how Daria and Persephone had stood at the mouth of the cave. I did not ponder why the Gods had chosen to reveal her to me or why the priestess had contrived that Daria and I should be involved in the re-enactment of a great tragedy. What interested me was the tragedy itself. I had seen the death of a world. I knew that what I had seen was not merely a significant and symbolic nightmare. I knew that the Gods send us dreams which are pictorial representations of our immediate predicaments and not revelations of cosmic truths. I wondered all the more what was the significance of this drama I had seen as I mounted the ladder of consciousness in losing my awareness of this world. I felt it to be all the more meaningful because I had returned to this world suspended in its own beauty, with the earth seeming silent and secure forever, locked in the majesty of its rocks and nevertheless scattered everywhere with fragments of its unshakable vitality, with the tide of blossom going through the darkness to the slope of the mountains, with the surreptitious ticking in the grass of insects intently alive in their simplified universe of moonlight and shadow.

When I spoke to the priestess my voice was languid and undemanding. I was still fatigued by the life I had lived in the depth of my unconsciousness. 'What I saw was the old story of Demeter relinquishing her daughter Persephone to Pluto, the God of the underworld. It is Winter when she is drawn into the darkness of the cave and Spring again when she returns to her mother. When she returns the corn is green and through incisions in the lava the earth is flooded with flowers.' As I heard my own voice I knew that I was still detached from myself, and in my detachment coming towards the heart of a great mystery. 'I believe that what I saw and felt was the combat between the forces of good and evil in the world. These forces are not abstractions pondered by the philosphers. Good and evil are less related to conduct than people imagine. They run like currents in the earth and either fertilize it or destroy it. The evil in our hearts and brains adds to the currents of evil vibrating in the earth. Sometimes the contrary occurs and the evil in our brains activates the currents in the earth so that we contaminate the ground we stand on. I believe that what I saw was a great earthquake and tidal wave. I believe that I saw the cave leading down to the underworld because Pluto attracted to himself all the evil around him and that without him there would have been no earthquake and no cave.'

'How could any man have had such a power of evil?' said Daria.

'I do not know any such man,' I said, 'But I feel I am right.'

'Is he right?' said Daria to the priestess.

'Yes.'

Daria was persistent. 'Is it possible for any man to be a living rod of metal conducting evil in this way?'

'Not in these days and on such a scale. Certainly it was once.'

'How long ago?'

'You will find that out later.'

I spoke again. 'When the corn grew and ripened and the flowers returned this was a sign of the force and vibrations of goodness in the earth. The few who survived the earthquake and lived on seaweed on the shore and on grass and lichen from the country did not see it as a blessing or as the sudden pity of a relenting and all powerful God. Because they were guaranteed life by the earth they saw the earth itself was a conductor of goodness. They felt there were channels in its dark substance which transmitted currents of goodness as blood flows in the vessels of the body. Goodness and evil to them were forces like the wind and fire, like sound and light. I believe that from those days there arose a belief in a power of good traversing the earth and the air above it and also in an insatiable and possibly greater power of evil. I believe also that because the evil arose from the earth the latter was created by a powerful entity in a dark mood or perhaps by one basically evil. I cannot believe any more that thunder and earthquakes are a sign of the anger of the Gods. I believe that the earth itself was created at a time of shadow by a dark entity who was nevertheless not wholly evil, because what he created had the power to nourish the flowers in Spring, the corn in Summer and to ripen the olives with the coming of Autumn. I believe also that Pluto had lived before. I do not know where or when but when he created the cave and engulfed Persephone he was living in a cycle of destruction and creation he had done before.'

For the most part while I was speaking the priestess was silent. I felt her silence as passive and receptive. I felt that the truth within my heart and hers was one and indivisible. I do not think she was speaking through me. I believe we were speaking as one and that in some way I knew all she had known and that we looked at the darkness of the world together. But now I saw her leaning forward and her features which had softened were hawklike again and I felt we were approaching some crisis in the to and fro tide of thought and feeling between us. 'You say that the world was created by a dark God in a dark mood. We have been told that the rocks of the world were thrown by the anger of Zeus.'

'No,' I said. 'I do not believe in our Gods as creators. I believe they were once men so constituted that they are enabled to come back to us and help us live. None of our Gods are creators. None made this earth.'

'There is a people living to the South across the water who believe that the God of their tribe is more powerful that the Gods of all others and that all He does is good. He is powerful and unrivalled and tolerates no others.'

'He must be an evil God.'

'His people hold Him to be good above all others.'

'Do they say He created this world?'

'Not yet,' she said. 'One day they will say also that all their God does is right.'

'Any God who made this earth created a world in which a woman writhes in agony when her child is born. To call such a God good is ridiculous. Nevertheless I know there is a God who created this earth because of the currents of good and evil which traverse it and which derive from an ultimate source. The God who created this world is a blind, bewildered creature. He is like ourselves because while he produces the broom and the flowering almond he kills also by tumours and storms at sea. Certainly he exists but he is not worth worshipping.'

Daria was looking up at me in fear and wonder. As she looked me full in the eyes her own seemed to darken and glow as though there was a great intensity of light in their darkness.

The priestess spoke again. 'That is the sum of your belief?'

'No. There is something behind the God the creator which you and I will never see because on this earth we are incapable of seeing past the Gods and Goddesses who are just men and women with the capacity to return having learnt a little more in Hades and the green fields of the shades. We cannot see or feel directly the presence of God because all Gods are creations of men. Artemis the Huntress comes back to me and moves in me because she is a woman and I am accustomed to respond to the beauty of women. But while I speak of Gods I am only thinking of and seeing men because, while the inner sight within us is more independent of the senses, what it sees is modelled on what we have seen by our perceptions on this earth. There is also a supreme influence which is like a force in that it directs the planets in their courses and arranges that in the end all things fall into a pattern and what was fragmentary becomes harmonious. But we cannot use a word like force to convey what is beyond the exercise of power and which is something like a divine imagining, as though the scents of flowers, the light of stars, the sound of music, the love of lovers, were all combined in an angelic something beyond sensation which showers down on the higher spirits all the manifestations of light and music which are filtered to us in this world and which we hear echoed in the sea and perceive a little lessened in ecstasy and light, in the first blooms of roses. All the beauty in the world is the farthest echo of something we cannot comprehend and which is beyond the creative capacity of whoever made this world.'

When I had ceased speaking Daria came to me and laid her hand gently on my shoulder. Then she took my hand in her own and at her bidding I rose to my feet. The priestess stayed seated but now she was hunched up and her face wilted and when Daria told me, 'This is too much for you. You are talking in a poetic language which is not your own,' I saw that indeed the priestess had been speaking through me, that my words and thoughts were not my own and that,

61

however much she insisted that I must see and feel things myself, what I truly felt within me was the reverberations of her own thoughts and of the echoing truths born and vibrating in the stars above us which had pierced to her heart and had been transferred to my own in the open and receptive condition which accompanied my moving beyond the frontiers of time.

Then the priestess rose slowly to her feet. When she moved towards me she was like an old woman and I saw that she was exhausted by what she had given me. She spoke like someone of legendary age who was plucking from the clouds of a past immeasurably far memories beyond the range of our minds. Now I knew that when she spoke, she was no longer hearing from me the re-echo of her own thoughts. She was imparting to me what she thought the ultimate distillate of her timeless experience. 'Remember,' she said, 'there is a power of good and evil in this world and the God who made it is himself a mixture of good and evil but chiefly evil. There is also an influence beyond the God who made this earth and this influence is feminine, without tarnish, unseen and never appearing in the form of a woman but always feminine. This is because woman is passive and all creation is passive. There is no masculine thought and intention in the making of the universe. The universe is the reflected projection of an image. It is no good arguing as to whether image or reality come first because in the pang of creation there is no time. What has come to us from millennia is the form of a woman Goddess revealed in light. In our day she comes mostly as Aphrodite the Goddess of Love but in other days she comes as Demeter. In the first days of Eleusis there were no male Gods. The highest realities of the universe came back to us as women. Demeter was gentler than the male God of the Jews who one day will replace her, claiming to have made the world in all its good and evil but insisting that all he has contrived is good. This is the great difference between the male God to be and the Mother Goddess and it is for this reason that I am speaking to you. The Mother Goddess knows that the world over which she presides is both good and evil. She makes a bargain with Pluto and submits to the evil of losing her daughter during the dark Winter of her soul. She does not insist, like the male Gods to come, in her total domination and that all she does is good. She does not wallow in the sufferings of her daughter in the cave and regard it as a great spiritual opportunity. She accepts it as a tragedy which she is

62

powerless to avert because being feminine, she does not think in terms of power. Remember above all that there are no safe or wholly moral Gods influencing this earth. We are safe and more in touch with reality in the arms of the Mother Goddess. Remember that Demeter compromised with evil in arranging that Persephone should live in the shadows of Winter and return to the light with the almond blossom. She recognized that there is a Winter of the heart which is sorrowful and evil. She knew that the compromise she made with Pluto was evil but she did it because she was close to man and the earth in the humanity left in her own heart and in the fecundity residing in her own tissues. By battling with Pluto she would have lost Persephone for ever. Out of her unheroic weakness the beauty and richness of the Spring was born. A male God would have believed that what he arranged with Pluto was good simply because he and Pluto had the power to make it. He would have disregarded the sufferings of Persephone and the Jewish God would have gone further and even decreed that suffering was good for her.' The priestess sighed heavily and I saw the circles deeper and lower beneath her deep-set eyes and the brown of her skin was now yellow and tarnished. She looked like a woman dying of a rapid decline and the sweat of weakness clung to her forehead. 'Now you should go home,' she said.

'Home, to the island?' I was astonished that she should seek to banish me from what I had sought for so long. 'Have I nothing to learn?'

'Very little.'

'Am I then so hopeless?'

'Not hopeless but the knowledge is locked up in your heart. For people like you there are places which act as keys but Eleusis is not one. There is a cave on your own island.'

'I know it. It is empty. Not long ago I saw a woman go inside it.'

'That is not possible,' she said.

'It is true. Do you think that what I saw was an hallucination in full daylight?'

'Yes.'

'You say that what I see when I lose consciousness is what has happened in the past. Why deny that I saw this woman walking the path to the mouth of the cave?'

'Because on this occasion you did not lose consciousness. You did not pass into the trance in which you see both what is true and old and what is more real than reality.'

'Do I pass into a trance when I smell the perfume of broom either out of season or at a distance and know that Daria is near?'

Her head slumped between her shoulders. When she looked at me her dark eyes were lightless and so dimmed by their own sorrow that I seemed to be looking at near empty sockets. I believed that she was both weary of me and at the same time intensely concerned for me. 'Have it as you wish,' she said. 'And you?' She turned to Daria.

'I will stay while he stays.'

After that day we did not see her for many days but we did not return to the island because I felt there was more to learn, but not from Eleusis and that the priestess herself had something more to tell us.

7

I NEVER thought to see again the dilapidated exquisite I had seen with his retinue going down the colonnade to the cave at Eleusis. I saw him again when I walked between the columns with Daria. He was returning from the cave where the priests and priestesses of Eleusis conducted their initiations. Behind him, watching him go, was the long-faced priest with the transparent skin and the washed-out eyes, who had seen so much virtue in Daria that he wished to unleash the power which resided in her virginity.

While we walked towards the cave I could see the priest smiling at us. At first his smile was directed at us both but afterwards it swung in Daria's direction like a beam of light from a lighthouse. His eyes were lighter. They did not catch fire like those of someone caught in a poetic emotion or walking in the shadow of the Gods. They glowed like embers reawakening from the ashes in which they were embedded. He raised his right arm slowly and beckoned to us. His arm, a flail of soft muscle, ascended loosely like a separate appendage. I knew that the gesture of his arm was not a welcome but a summons. 'He is asking for you. Don't go,' I said.

'I must go.'

'Priest of Eleusis or no I tell you he is evil.'

'That is why I must go.'

'We can pick up the evil which is radiated from the psyche.'

'Look at me,' she said. 'Do I look as if I would wither?' In the heat, in the palpitating rhythms of the heat haze, in the muffled dust which rose from the parched earth, she preserved her living pallor, flushed with rose, which came from some ancestor in the remote north where the snow was crystalline and heaped up to Heaven and where the women acquired the virginity of the wide-bosomed snow fields and the blue, liquid diamond of their intersecting waters. 'I am going for your sake,' she said. 'I am going because something is intended for us.'

I clutched her arm. I would not have let her go but just at that moment the over decorated princeling steered uncertainly towards me, the unnaturally soft flesh of his face descending in hanging cheeks that flowed into his neck and his rounded shoulders which merged with the beginning of breasts. His skin seemed congealed behind a coat of wax. I could not discover whether it was its natural texture or whether the glazed effect was produced by the creams and ointments with which he was anointed. His eyes were an astonishing and burning emerald. I have never seen their like in man or woman. It was not just an aesthetic but a physical shock to see something so burningly natural and indeed beautiful in the melting gills of his face. His threadlike hair was pale auburn. It looked as though it had been designed to crown the head of an impossibly innocent and sickly child. This creature waddled when he walked. His premature paunch slewed loosely sideways as he pirouetted obscenely in my direction.

I had no idea what he wanted of me. What I knew instantly was that he had been directed to me by the priest. I could see the latter, his arms still loosely suspended in the air and pointed at Daria. Now his fingers were crooked and it seemed to me that he was drawing her towards him. Meantime the animated mummy moved straight towards me. It was only when we were almost touching that he turned to Daria and flashed in her direction a carnivorous and comprehensive smile. I could see that in his mind he was already seething to have his will of her. Then he turned back to me. For me his smile was more subtle and formed slowly. Indeed, as he smiled there was a certain ruined beauty in the wreckage of his face. I think this weird counterfeit impression of beauty was in part hallucinatory. It derived from the emanation of his extraordinary eyes. 'I have heard so much about you,' he said. 'Perhaps we could sit down and talk a little.'

I looked at Daria not because I feared greatly for her but to remind him of her presence. In that moment she was my woman and I wished to emphasize it for his benefit. I had heard something of the Greek habit of confusing men and women in their sexual banquets. Such refinements had not as yet arrived on our island which was in any case within sight of Crete and took its customs from it. Daria had already gone from me. She was moving towards the priest and I felt in that moment that she and I were without identity, that between us was suspended a silver cord with which we transmitted what light we could, not because we were good but because we were made in a certain way and that this was expected of us. What light we transmitted was threatened by a great incurving wing of darkness. I felt that we were humans no longer but outposts of a battle conducted against the forces of darkness. 'Won't you sit down,' the monster added with an amiability which was toxic and resembled the emanations of a poison.

I could not see why I should do so but before I knew what had happened I was sitting on a stone seat cut out of the rock between two of the pillars of the colonnade. I was looking into his eyes, green, deeper green than the unscorched grass of Spring. I remember that the thought which came into my head at that moment was that whoever created the world threw in the enticement of beauty mixed with its worst elements. 'You have been pointed out to me before,' he said. 'I am so happy to meet you.'

'Who pointed me out?' Not even in Eleusis could I refrain from the brusquerie of my island speech.

'Ah, that would be giving away a secret.'

I knew all the time that there was no one else in Eleusis who could have directed him to me but the priest with the transparent skin, with the washed-out eyes and bloodless lips. I knew that the priestess would never have said a word about me. I was afraid of her and to me there was some dark mystery about her so that I could not entirely trust her but I felt that she was incapable of anything ignoble and if I could not trust her word entirely it was merely because I felt that she would always withhold the total truth from me. Always at the back of my mind was the conviction that I had access in a veiled way to a good deal of the wisdom in which she was steeped. I did not know how I came to acquire it and was prepared to believe that I was born with it. Or was it perhaps merely that I was one of the brighter products of a very small island and that my self-esteem was inflated?

'Why have you come to Eleusis?' he continued.

'To learn. Why have you?' I knew from the gold bracelets and the jewelled and ludicrously feminine fillet round his hair that he was a princeling of some sort but as he had no authority in my far-off island I spoke to him as bluntly as I would to any stranger asking me too intimate questions.

'Now why do you think *I* have come?' he said. His flabby face sunk into his half female chest and he exuded a wheezy, coy condescending friendliness as though he was speaking to a child.

'I have no idea.'

'Why do people come to Eleusis?'

'To learn,' I said wearily, 'and to be initiated into the Mysteries.'

'And which do you think I came for?' He jerked himself half upright like a sharply angulated doll. His arch manner was clownish. Had he been exhibited at a religious fête I would have found it funny. Combined with his prematurely aged face, which seemed to derive not from wear and tear but from rotting tissues, it was merely repulsive. Yet all the time, seeming to hover above his face, was the hypnotic compelling beauty and menace of his deep green eyes.

'The Mysteries, I suppose.' I said this merely because I knew that the Mysteries were designed for the elect and I knew this was the answer he was wanting. This thought first came into my head as a kind of reflex. This, I thought, is something he wishes to boast of. It is perhaps less boring for me to feed his vanity and escape as soon as possible. But then the full enormity of what I had thought came into my head. The initiations were only for those with spiritual gifts who had purified themselves by long preparation. They were a gift of the elect to the elect. Those on whom they were conferred acquired some of the insights and attributes of the priesthood. They were therefore, or at least in theory, specially selected men and women and I wondered how this creature, loose, sagging and as meaningless as a bundle of dirty clothing, could qualify for the sacred rites.

'Yes, the Mysteries,' he minced.

'Why do we wish to be initiated in the Mysteries?' My bewilderment made me more forthright than ever. I wondered suddenly how he endured my peremptory questions but I saw that he was sitting with his face half turned towards me and studying my profile carefully. I appeared to interest him more than I would have thought and it made me more wary than ever.

'I am a ruler in my own country. Of course that is not the whole story.'

'What has your being a ruler to do with the Mysteries?'

'Wouldn't you always want to be ruled by a good and wise man?' His voice was wheedling and his breath spasmodic. He resembled an old defeated prostitute persisting that she still had to sell something that was worth having. This half pleading, half demanding manner went ill with the jewels and ornaments spilt over him like a cosmetic lotion.

'Yes, I suppose you——' I could not ask him if he regarded himself as good and wise.

'To be initiated in the Mysteries confers great goodness and wisdom.'

'Is this what you want?'

'It is my duty to my people.'

'Oh,' I said. I did not see the connection.

'People will be willing to submit more freely to one they know to be good and wise.'

'And how would they know?'

'My dear boy, they would know because I have been accepted as an initiate.'

'And the initiates are carefully chosen?' At that moment I looked him fully in the face because the reek of perfume was stupefying.

While he moved some lace object draped in a circle round his forehead he added, with a self-satisfied and confident purr, 'They are always well chosen.' He emitted a spluttering laugh like the last cough of a dying fire and added, 'For an enlightened being you are slow at some things.'

'When you return to your people it will be obvious to them that you are transfigured?'

'Quite obvious.'

'How will this help you?'

'They will be easier to govern. They will pay their taxes better. You don't know how frankly dishonest some of them are. When they see that, though claiming nothing for myself, I have been accepted by people, well, semi-divine, they ought to be easier to manage. Lately they have been rebellious and at times bestial.'

Suddenly I felt distraught and hysterical. I wondered if his people had the same revulsion to perfume as me and if they were capable of staging a mutiny. Such thoughts as these were merely distraught amusements. I offered myself to act as an anodyne for the disappointment and pain I felt because of our vain visit to Eleusis. I had left the island feeling that the world would expand and that I would find confirmation of what I had felt in those moments when I paid for my visions in unconsciousness and other symptoms of the falling sickness. I felt a great revulsion to Eleusis and everyone in it. For a moment I hated the priestess especially. Surely her animated talk was misleading and a form of treachery seen against the background of what, rather illogically, seemed to me decomposing and rotten. But even as I hated the priestess, and, in the rising whirlpools of rage in my brain addressed bitter words to her, I felt her presence and almost saw the comprehending smile which softened her dark, all seeing eyes. At the same time I felt, between the pillars of the colonnade, the smell of broom, blown immeasurably far from the headlands of the sea and I knew that I was not smelling the odour of the flowers but receiving a signal from Daria by which she told me she was with me. I felt the burning low down in my abdomen which confirmed that she was present in the envelope of a non-physical body and I wondered how things went with her. I did not feel any fear for her because there was no fear in the perfume of the broom and I knew also by the aura low in my abdomen that she was sending aid to me.

It was at that moment that I felt his hand across my knee and knew why the smell of broom was stronger than ever in my nostrils and why Daria was, though somewhere with the priest, nevertheless also present behind my shoulder. 'Do you know that you are a very attractive boy,' my companion was saying. He was less of a monster now and more like a puppet manipulated by the strings of his incoherent lusts.

I was not in the least upset by his gesture. It affected me no more than would a lizard in my palm. 'Do you think I could be initiated?' I asked him. 'Would they accept me at the Temple?'

'I see no reason why not.' He leaned forward and breathed

heavily. As he did so the blood seemed to flow into his loose and advancing jowls and the lower part of his face was purple. 'You could rely on me to do all I could for you.' With feverish determination he moved his hand a little higher up my thigh. I had an almost uncontrollable impulse to laugh but somehow restrained it. I laughed not because I was a fleeting target of this monster but at all the hopes I had entertained wandering the woods and rocks of my far and beautiful island and expecting the world of Eleusis.

At that moment I was no longer interested in Eleusis or anyone in it. It seemed to me, leaping turbulently to a false conclusion, that what I had thought was a Mystery, that is to say a concentrated truth, was a cult like any other and that people only embraced it for what they could get out of it. I rose from the bench. 'Can't you stay a little longer?' the abortion whimpered.

'I have someone to see.'

'That pretty, no, that very beautiful girl.'

'You think she is beautiful?' I said. I was anxious to know if women were among his targets.

'Beautiful, beautiful.' He tried to restrain the succulence of his lips. 'But she belongs to you and I am a man of honour. Were we friends and could share——. But I am sure we could be friends.'

'Anything can happen in this world,' I said.

The mere fact that he wanted Daria did not sicken me. What was repellent was the visual picture of their bodies together, of the juxtaposition of the living pallor of her skin, like gold on her face, breasts and anywhere where the sun had touched it, with the airless, sodden flesh of his dropsical body. I thought of the fineness and elasticity of her features, of her face that could be as severe and watchful as the sculptured head of a Goddess but which came to life when the mouth widened in her red lipped, all enveloping smile. I thought of him bending over to kiss her and of his jowls spilling over and almost obliterating his small pursed mouth. I bade him goodbye and walked away to the half shadow of the pines from which I could watch the entrance of the Temple for Daria's return.

When she left the Temple she turned immediately to the left as though she knew by instinct where she would find me. She was as beautiful as ever but her eyes were withdrawn. Her beauty was always something outgoing and directed at others. You could read this in the poise of her head and the musing smile of her half opened lips. It was written chiefly in her luminous eyes. When she saw me she lifted and widened her hands and the light came back into her eyes. She ran the last steps towards me. 'Have you heard anything new?' I said.

'I have been offered initiation.'

'On what grounds?'

She laughed lightly. 'My exceptional talents. My capacity to emanate. And of course the gift of my body.' She laughed again. 'You see it was given to me and it seems I should offer it to others.'

'We heard this before.'

'It seems I have advanced since then. I have been offered an experimental experience.'

'With whom?'

'A priest.'

'This is indeed a mystery.'

'If it seems that I have the capacity to produce self-abandonment in men I would be initiated very quickly and would go on to initiate others.'

'Shall I show him to you?' I said.

'Please,' she answered. 'He is already in my mind.'

We walked together out of the shadow of the trees and across the elastic thyme-padded turf where we could look towards the colonnade. The princeling was still sitting smiling with vacant amiability at the sun as though he recognized it as a relative. He was biting his nails and from the way his lips twitched his mind was on more shadowy pleasures than the sun afforded. 'Yes, that is he,' she said.

'And the priest suggested you should give yourself to him?'

'Yes, yes.'

I could not control my anger and disgust. My emotions were so powerful and unharmonized that my stomach heaved and I thought I would vomit. 'Is this the refinement of the Dionysian frenzy? If so may the Gods help us. At least the Dionysians had the excuse that what they did was natural. What kind of a man is this priest that he would satisfy this creature with your body served up to him like a cold offering? Aren't you sickened and disgusted?'

'No.'

There was something so starry and remote in her serenity that I was infuriated by it. 'You do not mean to say you could ever hope to be mauled by this monster?'

'No, because no good would come of it.'

'Doesn't the thought of it make you want to vomit?'

'No, my love. Why ever should it?'

'Do you know that he also attempted to seduce me?'

'However lonely I will be I will not give myself to any priest or other man.'

'Why shouldn't you?' I said. 'After all this man doesn't revolt you.'

'No.'

'He is saturated with evil,' I said.

'Certainly I am not revolted by anything living because to be revolted is superfluous.'

'Then give yourself to him.'

'No.'

'Why?'

She was laughing no longer. 'Because it would do no good. He would be no better for it. He is incapable of improvement. He looks sodden with desire.' Now she had not only ceased to laugh but her eyes, now deeper blue than the sea, were fixed so relentlessly on mine that for a moment they were like those of the priestess in one of her more remote and unforthcoming moods. 'Also I am a virgin. I wish to choose myself the man who takes away my chastity.'

'Is that man still me?'

'Always. Unless of course you are going back immediately to the island.'

'I am sorry. I adore you. If I ever hurt you it is because I love you.'

'No, no.' Her eyes had a terrifying dark solemnity. 'Don't say you are sorry. If you try to atone you separate yourself from me. If we are one another we take each other's angers and jealousies as well as our loves.'

'Let us at least leave this place because it is evil.'

Her eyes widened with surprise. 'But it is most emphatically not evil. Is the priestess evil?'

'No,' I said reluctantly, 'but she is very mysterious.'

'As we came to learn from the Mysteries we can at least tolerate those who become mysterious in their practice. But Eleusis is not evil. It is the world in miniature. To me it is all men's thoughts and feelings in a concentrated form. It is a mixture of good and evil in high concentration so that we can learn more of each here than elsewhere.'

'But this is supposed to be a sacred shrine.'

'Nothing is sacred unless it portrays light overcoming darkness. It cannot do so unless there is darkness in the vicinity. If you want it I will start off for home with you this very moment.'

'Is there more for us to learn?' I said weakly.

'Yes, to learn,' she said, 'but that we should stay is written in the pattern.'

'You know this yourself?'

'I know things to the level I was born with. I shall learn no more. I was born into this world to see that you learnt and were hurt as little as possible in so doing.'

'You mean the Gods are kind?'

'I doubt it,' she said, 'I would say it was the Goddesses.'

Later that day we walked in the black and gold country with belts of corn between the pine trees. The gold of the corn drained the green from the trees and the country seemed in some way molten. There were rivers of gold in the corn between the trees. The corn was gold beside the dark lava of the forest through which the sun did not penetrate. 'In this country it seems as if the earth is moving. As we walk between the trees there is light and shade but when we look back it is black like lava.'

'These days you are always thinking about earthquakes,' she said. 'You talk of them in your sleep.'

'Is it the past which talks in my sleep?'

'Perhaps,' said Daria. 'That is one thing of great importance which you have learnt.'

'What is that?'

'That the Goddess Demeter who waited for her daughter after the great earthquake is the highest of the Goddesses and that which is beyond her is utterly supreme and more godlike than the Gods.'

I turned to her, suddenly afraid and needing reassurance. 'I sometimes wonder if the future talks also in my sleep. I see often the ending of the world. It comes, I think, in the death of our island. I see the conical summit sawn off from the mountain. I walk through the last green fields and the sea of lava rolls remorselessly towards me.'

73

At that moment the priestess stepped from behind a tree. She was not three paces from us. Her smile was so radiant that for a moment she was unrecognizable. The hardness had gone from her face. She gave no longer the impression of a wisdom which, coming as it did from someone with hawklike and hard-boned features, seemed almost predatory. 'You do not need to worry about the future whether you see it in your dreams or in visions by day. The future is only the echo of the past. The end and the beginning are the same because there are no ends or beginnings except in this world because the other worlds have dispensed with time.'

As she finished speaking the priestess's eyes lingered on mine. She kept looking at me, almost beckoning me towards her with her ineffaceable smile and with her mouth which I saw when relaxed to be deliciously provoking. Suddenly she moved and for a moment she seemed to be coming towards me with her hands widened to embrace me but at the last moment she veered suddenly to Daria and threw her arms round her and kissed her warmly. 'I kiss you for both,' she said. 'I kiss you because it is your destiny to care for him. I know that to take second place is to be first,' she added. 'Do you understand this?'

'A little, in a way.'

'It is the lot of woman to see a man develop and perhaps go from her. These things mean nothing. She is always higher than he is because she moves less.' She turned to me. 'Is there anything you want to know?' she said. It was the first time she had encouraged me to ask questions.

'Yes. I would like to know what the priest means by pressing Daria to give herself to this abortion of mankind.'

'You ask the priest yourself.'

'But you can answer, you yourself are a priestess.'

'How do you know I will answer the same?'

'But surely what are called the Mysteries are changeless and inviolable. Those admitted to them must share the same knowledge and see life in the same way.'

Suddenly the priestess's face hardened and went pale. She swung swiftly round and looked along the path she had come by between the trees. 'There is no one near but it is not necessary to court danger.'

'What danger is there?' I asked.

'I cannot tell you. I cannot interfere with the pattern of destiny which is being woven. I can only help you a little at times when you are entangled in it. But from now on our meetings must be secret.'

'Why?'

'Secret,' she said. 'No one should ever ask why unless he himself has the answer in his heart.'

'Where do we meet?'

'Here,' she said. 'Two nights from now at high tide and midnight.' She went away from us between the trees.

'What could she mean?' I said to Daria.

'Oh, anything,' she said. I was certain that Daria knew more than I did. She fed me wisdom in reluctant fragments. This was something I never resented. I knew that all I would ever value would be what I had first evaluated myself.

8

I SAW the priest one day when I was walking some distance from the temple in a country of white sand which suggested the nearness of the sea which was actually some distance from it. There was a hollow in the earth which in that place was shaped like a bowl. I moved from the darkening of trees which made the rim of the bowl and walked towards the pond made stagnant by the thickness of the rushes which grew in the water. Many paces from the pond I could smell the scent which arose from the thick dark clusters of mint which grew at its margins and invaded the shadows. In the heat were glittering points where the sun was reflected from particles of mica in the sand's burning pallor. It was an empty, after-death country and the smell of the mint was a memory in paradise of a living world from which one was now excluded.

The priest came undulating towards me. He was thinner than I thought and his shadow on the white sand was a long dark spire which had fallen to earth but which retained some serpentine quality and moved towards me. As he came near his face seemed longer than when I saw him last and his skin more than ever like the tense, stretched transparent gut of an animal. His washed-out eyes were glazed in a kind of stupor of loneliness and artificial affection. He welcomed me with a sad, beseeching smile. I had heard that some could reincarnate as animals. I wondered if some creating God had hesitated for a moment between a man and a fish and if the priest had been conceived in an instant of cosmic hesitation.

We talked for a little while of the country around us, of the mint by the pond, of the thyme thrown in dark cushions against the sloping sides of the white bowl where the sand receded and where the soil was thicker. He spoke of the use of herbs as medicine. He spoke with compassion of the sick and I was almost persuaded that he meant what he said. His soft, floating hands made so many pensive, helpless gestures as though he recognized the limits of the good he could do, as though his heart bled in contemplating his own impotence. At these moments his head was bowed on his chest. His nodding head and floating hands made a kind of harmony in which he lamented the pain of the world and that his heart bled for so much that his hands were powerless to aid.

After he had spoken of the herbs and medicines and the goodness of the earth he spoke also of greater benefits borne less in the earth than in the sun and the stars and how these could be diverted to the benefit of mankind. Of course this could only be done through the Gods. The latter with their understanding and natural generosity were prepared to divert these benefits to men. This could only be achieved through chosen agents because in the wrong hands the powers of the Gods could be so diverted as to exercise an infinite power for evil.

This puzzled me a little. 'What,' I said, 'are the names of the evil Gods? I always understood that the scourges of the world were inflicted by ordinary Gods with which we are familiar when they were angry because of our transgressions or just because they were angry.'

'That is so,' he said, 'but there are also dark causes of which men know little. They are so dark,' he added with sudden animation, 'that perhaps it is best they have no name.'

'There is always Pluto,' I said. 'He is, after all, the God of the underworld.'

'An inferior God but not wholly evil.' The priest waved a white hand to dismiss as effortlessly as possible the accusation of evil. 'After all he gave to Demeter the secret of growing corn.'

Sitting with him on a rotten tree trunk within sound of the deep-noted glug of the water fowl cruising serene in the still dark water there were two thoughts only in my head. One was that he believed in the force of evil as much as I did but that he had achieved the right knowledge for the wrong reasons and that he was engaged in fitting his belief, like the fragment of a mosaic, into an infinitely greater and more impressive conception. My second thought was that I was in danger but that here, in this place, my duty was to sit with him and hear him impatiently, seeming to agree, and that I must stifle completely any urge to play the role of the island iconoclast. 'I suppose it is very necessary for you to control the force of evil,' I said. I myself believed it to be uncontrollable but I felt certain that I could not afford to say it.

'Very necessary,' he said. 'The Gods are of course close guardians against the force of evil.'

I could not see how this could be, seeing that the Gods themselves were an adulterated vintage but I knew I had best keep silent. 'Then come the priests of Eleusis. We learn the control of evil through the Mysteries. But we alone are not enough to contain the evil of the world and ensure good government.' This was the first time he had mentioned government and I pricked up my ears. 'It is therefore necessary that men of authority, provided of course they are of moral worth, should partake of the Mysteries and acquire strength from their initiation.' This, I thought, is where the monster comes in. He is included under the heading of moral worth. 'As well as these there are young men – and women – with special gifts.' He added the word women as a markedly delayed afterthought. 'These are recruited to fill the necessary gaps. This is why we were interested in you and the beautiful girl with you.' Once again the loose tentacle of his arm floated in the air but when it descended its touch on my knee was not accidental but artistically contrived. He did not prolong it but I had at that moment the feeling that he differed from the princeling in preferring his own sex. My multi-coloured admirer was less exclusive in the satisfaction of his affections.

I thought of what the priestess had told me of the nature of the Mysteries and how she had never indicated that their study was in any way connected with the maintenance of order and with secular authority. I assumed the deliberately enlightened rather stupefied look I employed when I wished to terminate conversation with my father by conveying the impression that he was blunting the fine blade of his intelligence against the recalcitrant rock of my natural stupidity. 'So without the Mysteries the people perish,' I said. 'Without a regular flow of initiates there would be a complete breakdown of law and order.'

'No priest could have expressed himself better.'

'It is odd that so many priestesses remain in Eleusis. Do women lend themselves particularly well to the maintenance of law and order?'

'This brings us to the heart of the matter.' He drew a little closer to me. I felt wafted across towards me from the pond the scent of mint, dank, rich and astringent and I longed with all my heart for the lighter more persuasive odour of broom and for the presence invisible or otherwise of my love Daria. 'The women priestesses are useful, they are almost irreplaceable for the healing functions we have discussed. They are also irreplaceable for the induction of oneness through the body which is one of the rarest of all gifts and with which your friend is endowed in full measure if she only deigned to use it. These are the two main functions of the women priestesses. There are some who say that they should confine themselves to these spheres.' He moved his hand airily, deprecatingly, and it was obvious that he had already confined woman and locked her up within the narrowest frontiers of activity. 'Of course there are women initiates with a philosophical capacity equal to those of men but such are inevitably few. One stands out in my mind. You have met her already, the priestess Ekko. I seem to remember that you have sat and spoken with her.'

'She was interesting,' I said with careful diffidence, 'but I did not gain anything new from talking with her. Naturally I did not speak of the deeper issues. I am not interested in healing and as she offered no new potion for my own illness we did not have a great deal to say to each other. But tell me,' I continued, gazing more vacantly than ever into his eyes which seemed an ideal receptacle for the void in my own, 'wasn't there a time when the priests of Eleusis were largely women?'

'They were all women,' he said graciously, 'but that was a long time back. We have come on since those days. You see, in those times there was a great deal of undefined mysticism about the cult. You know what I mean, you know the nature of woman, there was nothing concrete and definite. There was no question of this man having qualified for initiation and receiving this access of strength from it. There was no proper utilization of the symbols.' He stopped suddenly here and his face sharpened to see if I had seized on his words. He felt he had gone too far. 'And of course I suppose the sexual element must inevitably have been more marked.'

This, I thought, was where he deteriorated to common lies. We all knew that, speaking in physical terms, the Mysteries of Eleusis were the grading down and the imposition of discipline on the drunken Dionysian frenzies. They were also a further development of the relative refinements of the Orphic cult. From what I had seen of the Dionysian fêtes in my own times, now reduced to certain days and chiefly nights of the Spring, it was no use telling me that the sexual element of the Mysteries had been instigated by the women. Certainly the women were its target, certainly they had been conditioned to respond and certainly those most possessed by a diversity of men prophesised sometimes liberally but I could not say with what accuracy. But to say that the primary instigation of these rites was feminine was absurd. I had seen my father, whose customary expression was of an educated sheep, transformed by a slim wreath of vine leaves round his hair and a fat flagon of wine in his hand into a combination of satyr and fertilizing machine to which household women submitted for no other reason than that they had to. 'In what way do you think the Mysteries will change in the future?' I asked.

'The Mysteries will never change,' he said. 'It is the organization of the Mysteries which changes now.'

'More men, less women.'

'That is how it has evolved,' he said. 'Of course naturally and without willed intention on the part of the priests. You will understand there is no intention to exclude women. For instance we all deplore that Ekko is leaving us.'

It was on the tip of my tongue to say that she had never told me. I restricted myself to simply asking 'Why?'

'She feels that she is not filling her duty as a woman because she has no gift of healing and no capacity for what we can call transcendental physical contact. As I have said she has great philosophical interests and aptitudes and we have tried to persuade her to stay with us. Her reason for leaving will strike you as significant. She says that she believes the role she plays is unwomanly and would be best served by man. We will be very sorry to lose her.'

'Where is she going?'

'She is returning to her home in Crete.'

'What will she do?' I asked.

'A woman of her degree of culture will always be a great influence for good.'

I looked at the white sand seething at my feet. It was ticking with life. It was swarming with small insects and, parched by the heat and drought of decades, innumerable particles of sand slid over each other and one seemed to be looking at the same insatiable molecular life as was alive in one's own tissues. I looked up from the earth towards the pond. The scent of the mint was borne suddenly and unaccountably on a breeze so cool that it was as if Autumn had come to a wider world. I felt the coolness of the stars in the heat of mid-day. Then the dank incense of the odours of mint and of the sunless shrubs lurking in the shadows of the rushes, was dispersed in an inaudible current of air. I smelt the broom and the vapour of morning lifting from the high hills and saw Daria coming towards me, smiling, walking eagerly and with enthusiasm, totally undeterred by the presence of the priest, even smiling at him with the same glowing, wide eyed, wide mouthed friendliness that seemed expended not on him and me only but on the world itself.

She sat at the end of the log so that the priest was between us. I did not resent him at all because the air was changed and I was living in a world more real than reality. In this new world she was with me not in the flesh but as a touchstone. It was astonishing to look to the right and see her profile and the gentle protrusion of her breasts beneath her tunic. When she came to Greece she had covered her breasts. I felt that the priest was uneasy. He moved nearer towards me. As a Greek and a priest he was less comfortable in the presence of women than we who were nourished in the ways of Crete.

Then the world changed and in front of me there was no aching white sand and no dark edge of pines pencilled sharply along the rim of the hollow in which we sat. Between me and the hills with their thin scrawl of pines the air had darkened. I could still feel the sunshine and heat on my forehead but between me and the low tide of forest was a palpitating veil. It was grey at first but the vibration of half light slowed down and soon the veil congealed in a chamber with dark walls arching sharply above so that the roof converged into a point. What seemed a cascade of light descended from the walls. I saw that, from the floor to the beginning of the arch, they were covered with mirrors of burnished metal. The metal was faced with silver and the light reflected from it converged upon a blunt small altar. The final concentration of light was so blinding that I could not look at it for more than an instant. On the summit of the altar was a dolphin outlined in blinding silver and as I watched an ear of corn fell from the mouth of the dolphin. Then the light went from silver to gold and radiated, not from the dolphin but from the ear of corn. I knew that what I was looking at was the resurgence of the earth after the great cataclysm and the coming of the light in the corn in Spring. I knew that the Mother Goddess was in the silver light and that the corn coming from the dolphin was her ultimate womb. I knew that the dolphin was shining silver because he had carried the sun God Apollo to quicken the young corn and to warm the heart of Demeter as she waited for her daughter.

I knew that I was looking at a performance of the Mysteries. I heard the priest breathe sharply in a hiss by my side. I saw undefinable fear in his eyes and the sweat forming on his forehead. I knew that Daria was reading his mind and drawing from him what he knew of the Mysteries. I knew that I, too, through her was reading his thoughts and that what I was enduring was a repetition of the Mysteries but unknown to those who presided over them. I knew also that the priest was unaware of the nature of the fear that gripped him. He knew that vitality was being sucked from him and by a woman and hated her for it but he did not know that by telepathy she was divulging the Mysteries to me.

Then there was no longer the alternation of silver and gold shining on the dolphin and the ear of corn. There was suddenly the billowing out of a dark curtain and after than an alternation of dazzling silver light and total blackness and I knew that, by a play of mirrors and hidden lights in niches, they were reproducing for us the forces of good and evil, the light and dark in the world, in rapid succession. I knew that this, and the dolphin and the ear of corn, were only a symbolization of the powers of good and evil and of the con- taminated creation of the world. Such representations were useful for people who visited Eleusis and could say later that they had had a glimpse of the Mysteries but to whom only the outward ceremonial was revealed. I knew also that hidden in larger alcoves – and the smaller niches containing shining and illuminated glasses which gleamed and were obscured and manipulated by the acolytes – there were priests and priestesses but mostly priests who by an intense concentration of the psyche within them could take man back through the light of life to the darkness preceding birth. The priests did this because they were trying to elude time, to evade their personalities and to heal in their psyches. This is what I myself did, passively, helplessly and unknown to myself when, before and after my attacks of unconsciousness, or during dreams when my illness was upon me, I could see into the future and the past.

Sitting in the bright sunlight, dimly aware of the rim of the forest opposite but peering always into the dark crucible of life in front of my eyes and which I now saw to be shaped like the opening of the female cavity, I knew that the priests were, by a concentration of their psyches for which they had trained for years, taking the initiate back to the first years of his life. I myself, though I had no power concentrated on me and received only the echo of the initiation, saw what had been significant in my life. There was first the bloated face and sagging intestines of the creature sitting in the colonnade. For a moment he occupied and obliterated the bright screen before me and I wondered how so recent and repulsive an acquaintance could be so important to me. Then I saw Daria coming over the hill. This I could understand better. She brought with her the light of morning and the illuminated and panting web before me was sprinkled with particles of crystal from the light behind her. Then, before the coming of Daria, I saw many things I had forgotten, like a swelling apple with a deep red skin which was somehow a world that died at sunset. When the stars came out the sea was alone and the land had receded. Then I saw, with such tenderness that I wept, Electra bending over me and stroking my forehead. She could have been no more than eight at that time. I was only six. We sat together in the wood with my head on her not yet budding breasts. She played her favourite game of being my mother. Staring across the heat haze reflected from the pitiless glare of the sand I heard her voice as clear as though I lay once again with my head on her breast. I knew at that moment that, in the end, she would be nearer me than the others,

82

still with her arms outstretched and still regretting she had never been my mother.

Then I saw the face of my father on a night in Spring, fundamentally lugubrious and ridiculous but dusted over like a clown's mask with a thin dressing of hilarity, with his wreath of vine leaves perched on his forehead but draped drunkenly over one eye, basking in the mindless and ritualistic adulation of his slaves and pulling with sweating hands a tall woman with a still face into the darkness of a thicket of myrtle and bay surmounted by what in the night was the carved, inevitably classical outline of a huge holm oak. I heard him disappear in a crash of brushwood. Then I heard the woman's cry, the rustle of brushwood and the tumult of tree branches and after that the shuddering silence more frightening than the storm in the trees from the thrash of branches. Then I heard a sharper cry from the woman and later a slow moaning. I saw her in travail with her legs drawn up and after that I myself was inside the darkness and my narrow, dark world was contracted about me. I knew that I had struggled to be born, that I myself had returned to the womb and darkness and that this was the most I knew of my mother. I felt I had seen enough.

I do not know how I restrained the scenes coming to my head from passing to Daria and the priest. I think I had the power to do so because, as I see now, I was born an initiate. My falling sickness was the memory both of my struggle to be born and, later, my rebirth as an initiate. Many of my attacks of unconsciousness in which I saw the past and the future were a return to the Mysteries in which I had been initiated. Then I saw that in looking to the past I must have looked many times beyond my own birth. It came to me in a flash that here was one of the ultimate mysteries transmitted only to the deep initiates at Eleusis. We had lived before on the earth and returned many times to it. At that moment I was back once again in the dark, pulsating cavity of my mother's womb, of the world of my own destiny, seeking for the life that had been mine before I came to the island. I saw a white cloud race horizontally across an impossibly blue sky. When it had passed there was a temple on a hill in the dawn of Summer, a grove of pines and a spring which poured out ice-cold water from the parched earth not yet fissured and wrinkled by the heat of Summer. I saw women in light blue robes and heard the music of flutes and the falling of water. I knew that this was the time when all was unsullied. I longed to stay in this world of low hills away from the heat of the plain, where people moved slowly and where the messages were addressed to the heart from the wind in the trees and the murmur of the river. But a voice which I recognized as the priestess Ekko cried out sharply, harshly, 'Not yet, not yet. Come back to your own world and stay quietly in it.'

So I came back to my own world slowly, through the thoughts of Daria which were drawn from the black and white whirlpool of memories and rituals in the priest's inexplicable and clouded mind. I came back through my struggles in the body of whoever was my mother, through the childhood love which Electra gave me and by which she was now tortured, to Daria coming over the hill, her tunic light golden like the sun of morning and even to the perfumed mass of flesh who had tried to seduce me outside the temple. I could not understand why the light lingered so long on the floating fat of his body, on his waddling shapeless thighs and why he was suddenly moaning on the ground and crying, 'Alone, alone. You must send her to me.'

I turned suddenly to Daria. I had two pictures of her as one gets of a face reflected in angled mirrors. In one she was sitting on the log with her lips parted in a half smile and looking lovingly towards me. On the other she was walking naked across a mosaic floor decorated by dolphins performing their silver convolutions in a mild blue sea. The monster lay at a corner of the mosaic, and her eyes, looking at him as he writhed and moaned, and cried that he was alone, were as loving as when she looked at me. Then there was a sudden, vertical shaft of white light, a vague feeling of the priestess being near and receding from us to the jagged shadows of the rushes in the pond, and I sat on the log with the sweating and bewildered priest and Daria played with a sprig of scented daphne. She seemed as happy as the day was long.

I rose slowly, almost luxuriously, from the log. I had never been so tired in my life but a great peace had come over me. I was also very afraid but in some way the terror was at a distance. I could hold it back if I stretched out my arm. I felt at peace because I believed that I had seen beyond the Mysteries to the source and significance of life itself. How could there be Mysteries except for those who desired to maintain them in order to exercise power over others? There could be delicately shared, non-compulsive secrets of which you spoke

84

only to your friends because they were made as you were. You could speak together of the same Goddesses you had seen, knowing that your memory would reinforce that of another but this was an altogether different affair from the aimed intensive searching now practised at Eleusis. I knew in that moment that there was a limit to the degree to which we can train people. You can condition and relax their bodies and purify their senses so that the softer winds are heard more acutely and you can smell the odours of thyme at a greater distance. You can enable people to lie more at rest in the shade of trees in the noon of Summer and to feel and learn more from the heartbeats of the earth. In such moods the psyche of the dead and of those who love us and who speak to us from a distance can approach us more closely, telling what they have learnt and what is still unknown. Beyond this one should not go.

But however wisely I thought I had already been taken beyond what I had seen, I had been drawn into the Mysteries by the force whirling at their periphery. I had to take care that I was not sucked in by the power which draws us to the heart of the whirlpool.

I thanked the priest for his conversation, his patience and his courtesy. I said I had understood much, that I had appreciated for the first time how much the health and welfare of the community depended on those who administered the Mysteries. 'You make me happy,' he said. 'What I can do for you I will do to the utmost of my ability.' His smile was truly beautiful. Anyone's smile is beautiful once or twice in a lifetime, in those particular moments when they are receiving in full measure what they desire most. When he turned to Daria his smile was this time impossibly beautiful. 'You, too,' he said. 'I will help *you* in any way I can.' He turned to me again, pressing my hand in a gesture which was not repulsive but pathetic because it expressed his deep hope and half belief that he had made contact with me. 'Do remember,' he told me, while smiling at Daria, 'that I have still great hopes for this child and that what I said about the limitation of women priestesses applies in no sense to her.'

We parted the best of friends. I was still at peace even though I saw Daria, beautiful in her nakedness, like gold where the sun had poured down the length of her long limbs, moving towards the stuffed and painted doll who, when I last met him, had tried to seduce me and who, seen in the Mysteries, was half mad and agonized. For the time being I did not worry about Daria because I had already been taken out of time. To sit with her and look across the cornland to the belt of pines was to come back slowly to the world and rediscover leisurely, deliciously, separate beauties in the harmony in her which used the glow of her eyes and the line of her dress to express an abstract principle of beauty and womanhood beyond the flesh, beyond the conceptions of the brain, beyond even the echo of my deepest heartbeats.

9

WE went to the priestess at midnight. The night was well chosen and the moon was full. We walked from the forest to the sea. In the hour after midnight the light was still tawny on the trunks of the pine trees. Though it was not the time of harvest the light of the moon was deep and gold and its glow between the pines spilt on the earth like light from a fountain. The light seemed to tauten and intensify the light of the earth. Though the night was warm the soil crackled under our feet like frost. We walked through the forest to the sea. Across the sea the track of the moon was traced in silver. With the light of the moonbeams the blue of the sea was deeper and warmer than the blue of night.

'It is time for you to go,' the priestess said. 'It may even be that you have left it too late already.'

'No one can detain us.'

'It is possible. Those who might detain you are subject also to the pattern of destiny.'

'You see danger for us?' I said.

Her voice dropped to a whisper. 'You will arrive safely home on the island.'

Suddenly my throat tightened with tension and anguish. 'And Daria?' I felt her swept from me like a light extinguished. I felt the cloud of menace between us.

Ekko laughed gently. 'You and Daria will return safely to the island together.'

Now that the shadow of this fear had passed from me the world was again the world and I saw the thin pencils of shade slanting on the road from the long pines and the sand itself white in the moonlight and shelving gently to the dark blue sea. 'I am saddened by Eleusis,' I said. 'It is not what we expected.'

'You came too late. Soon you will see it as it was.'

'There will be reforms? A return to some earlier simplicity?'

She looked at me quickly, intently and then looked away. 'I only said you will see it as it was.'

'Do you mean we should come back to Eleusis?'

'You will see it as it was. There is no need to return. Through the priest and Daria you saw your struggle to be born. You can go back beyond it to another existence.'

Walking with the priestess by the sea I was aware only of her and little of Daria. Ekko had for me in those moments the same impersonal beauty as the silky moonbeams stroking the surface of the sea. In that hour after midnight, with the moon gold in the high heavens and silver where its reflection touched the sea, it seemed that she and I were inseparable from each other, that she was uncorrupted and unremitting, that about her there was a purity and hardness like the bleached rocks confronting the sea. I reached my hand towards her. It surprised me that she allowed me to touch her. In the warmth of that Summer night her fingers were icy but there spread from them up my arm the pulsation aroused in my own blood and I knew that wherever she was she would always direct me. Suddenly, illogically, I said aloud, 'I feel you are older than the sea.'

'We have as many lives as the sea has waves.'

'But when you say it,' I said, 'your eyes are tired and already there is a fan of wrinkles about your eyelids.'

'We return in the body. The psyche continues. This is one of the mysteries hidden from those who come here only to be partially initiated and are wholly revered when they return to their own cities. The same psyche returns in other bodies. That is why in the Mysteries they instruct by taking you beyond your own birth to the last death before it and on and on.'

'That itself would take an aeon,' I said.

'It is for that reason that the Mysteries are corrupt. They seek to do in days or months what merits the expiration of years.'

'This priest I spoke to sitting on the log was evil,' I said.

'No. You are too prone to see things as good and evil. He is a mixture like us all. He is corrupted but he did not contaminate himself. Had he served at Eleusis two centuries earlier he would have been a force for good. He is the victim of the system. His interest in healing is genuine. When he speaks of the potentialities of women it is something he believes in and feels in his heart but which cannot grow within him because his soul is caged in the iron of dogma. When he speaks of women being inadequate as symbols of authority he knows deep within him that there is no authority other than the heart and that the psyche records its pulsations for all eternity. This man is solely a creature of the Gods. What he seeks is to exclude the Goddesses from his heart. For this reason he is dedicated to driving the priestesses from the Temple at Eleusis.'

She paused and sighed and resumed very gently. 'Every woman carries in her heart the pity she has learnt from the helplessness of infants. Even if she has had none of her own she can still feel the muffled heat of her compassion. It extends from her own soul to that of the priestesses and Goddesses and finally to the Mother Goddess and beyond even that finality to the supreme essence which is feminine like the earth fertilized by the rain, like the sea played on by the moon so that her breast heaves in the great tides.

'Is there something beyond even the Mother Goddess?'

'There is an eternal feminine principle which is the source of all art, all philosophy, all truth and all healing. It is feminine because of its capacity to create. In terms of nature man is almost a superfluous animal. He has a minute's frenzy, transformed by the woman into a life which may last seventy years. Doesn't this surpass the momentary magic of a man fertilizing a woman with his seed? Isn't the superiority of man merely a testimony to his own aggression?'

'Tell me more of this eternal feminine principle.'

'I cannot tell you more because you and I are looking at what is unseeable from too far off. This is one of the things which can only be learnt after death. None of us here know more of the ultimate feminine principle except that it is a tensionless node from which issue all the vibrations of healing, love, beauty, philosophy and art.'

'And all this is being destroyed?'

'It cannot be destroyed but it can be veiled for centuries. Listen, my child.' It stabbed me to the heart when she said 'my child'. 'In this world we must choose between truth and magic. At Eleusis we had the truth but then it changed to magic. When the priestesses have all been expelled or have died of the desert inside their hearts there will be nothing here but a belief in grace from the Gods dispensed by priests and designed to strengthen the strong for the control of the weak.'

'Do you call the light in the dolphin and the ear of corn magic? It seemed to me beautiful and in a way sensible.'

'These things *are* beautiful,' she said. 'They are not magic when they are used to illustrate a truth or to stimulate gently a mood in which we become more receptive to it. They become magic when they are injected with the principle of power and with the need to hurry, when they are mixed with incantations and exhortations and hurried glances at the last assortment of initiates chosen because of their births and riches or because they are the raw material of priests.'

'I find it hard to understand,' I said.

'It is not to be understood. It is something to be seeing. It is only given to a few to see. This is a law of nature. All see in the end but for most people the process extends over aeons. It is evil to hasten the process of seeing. You will not do that. What is a human error not amounting to evil is to seek to understand by reason what is hidden in the Mysteries. This is the plaything of the amateur of salvation. You do it a little even though with you it is not necessary.' She turned to Daria. 'Come, take his hand and I will hold him too. He is a man and a child and therefore needs to be led.'

Walking with Daria holding my right hand and Ekko my left I looked not at the sea but at the land and forest and beyond the dark treetops to the hills. I could see the silver haze where, under the moonlight, the olive groves heaved to the slopes of the mountains. I could see the darkness of the near trees, the grey scrawl of tree trunks in the distance. I could smell the odour of the shrubs, piercing in the stillness of night and coming up more sharply to my nostrils as our feet brushed the tussocky thyme. I heard the minute clang as the dry leaves of the dwarf oak closed behind me. At the same time I saw, with my inner eye, beyond the mountain which barred the horizon, to a trough of land that heaved like the sea and beyond it to low hills with groves of pine trees. Still farther I saw a plateau with a high rock with a white temple perched between its crevices and close to the temple a singing spring. The water came out as translucent and unflawed as a diamond under the high moon. It poured in a sheet over the rocks and sang in the ravine that descended circuitously between the pine trees. Then the moon went down and dawn came with the birds singing and the water translucent and sparkling no longer but mysteriously silver. With daybreak I saw more clearly the lines of the temple and, under its arches, a long colonnade with smaller columns and along its length people stretched on pallets. There were women in light blue robes moving between the sick laid on the pallets and men similarly attired but the women were more numerous. I saw also, in niches in the overhanging rocks, with entrances shaded from the sun by green waving ferns, what seemed to be miniature temples with inside each a pallet and a sick man or woman lying on it. With each sick man was a woman in light blue or sometimes a man but always the women predominated.

All the mouths of the niches in the circle of the rocks were turned to face the spring and the rivulet descending from it. The sound of the water was resonant between the circle of rocks and I understood that part of the treatment of the sick was the echo of the spring from the rock and that the falling water was used as a narcotic. I saw the figures in blue robes raising and letting fall the limbs of the sick. Sometimes a raised arm was stiff and resisting but with the manipulations of priestly hands, themselves moving with the ease of seaweed on shallow water, the limbs of the sick became torpid and heavy. With the peace come to their limbs and over their bodies they breathed more deeply, and with the relaxation and closing eyelids induced by the deeper peace, the music reflected like light from the rocks entered their hearts and their eyes closed in a half trance that was not seeing or oracular but purely peaceful. I saw then that the siting of the temple and the colonnade in relation to the rocks, the spring, the rising and falling of the sun and the moon had been chosen because here all the elements of nature were vibrating at their most peaceful. 'That was all it was,' I said aloud, speaking to myself but aware that, whether the words were uttered or no, the priestess beside me would understand them. 'All that they did in healing was to achieve peace by submission to nature.'

'That was the beginning,' the priestess said.

'It was the beginning for all who came to the temple. Some came to be healed and after the relaxation and peace induced in their limbs by movement and non-movement there was also the laying on of hands in particular places. Here is one who lies still and whose brow suddenly darkens with the memory of an old agony. He struggles to the light and the priestess in blue lays a hand on his forehead and neck and the turmoil goes from him. Here is another whose heart is failing. A hand is laid on his chest and a little colour creeps back to his cheeks as furtively as the first flush of roses and the first light of day. Here is another with sunken cheeks and without power, so that when his hand is lifted to test its tension it falls back with a thud, weighed down by its own weakness as well as the degree of its relaxation. This one has a hand laid on the great plexuses in the gap where the lower ribs arch away from each other.'

For a time I was silent because what I saw next was inexplicable and frightening. I tightened my clasp on Daria and the priestess's fingers. Now the scene was different and all the peace gone out of it. A sick man had risen from his bed, haggard and hating, his hands clutching the throat of a young priest in white robes who had sunk to his knees before him. 'There is a man in white robes in great danger,' I said.

'Who is the man?' said Ekko.

'How should I know? It is five hundred years back.'

'No, you cannot know him,' Ekko said softly. I felt Daria squeezing my fingers more tightly.

Leaning over, the sick man exerted his pressure on the young priest's throat. The latter seemed to be dazed and lay rigidly on his back, his eyes revolving downwards and inwards, and his arms and legs stiffening. He parted his lips and a harsh screech that was not a cry but the complaint of a misused instrument issued from him. His back was so arched with the iron-hard stiffness of his muscles that it was lifted off the ground and he lay like a bent pole. Then his rigidity was sucked from his limbs and his legs and arms rattled convulsively and his blue lips foamed.

'Do I look like that?' I cried suddenly.

Ekko stroked my fingers. 'Not in this life, my child. All that remains of your illness is the loss of consciousness and the separation from the world which becomes before and after. And a little headache and giddiness and with it the seeing into the past and the future.'

'Why didn't you say this was me?' I cried. 'I swear that the man in the white robes was me.'

'Yes, my child,' said Ekko. Daria continued to squeeze my fingers.

'And this hill, the shape of the rock, the singing of the water, the niches and the toy temples within them, I have seen these for years, every Summer in childhood and mostly when the moon was full.'

'You saw in dreams what you have lived before. This is important. In your case you did not learn quickly of your past lives. To do so is almost always a disaster. You were born with the memory of them. This is the last you lived in and endured. What else do you see? Can you go beyond the past or would you rather stay with Daria and me and listen to the murmur of the sea?'

But even as she spoke there was no choice for me. I saw myself, my cheeks engorged, the white of my eyes red with the small vessels injected and staring up at the ceiling with an expression of frightened stupidity as the colour receded from my engorged cheeks and the hideous protuberance of my purple lips. Standing above me was the sick man, his face transformed, not outlined in light but transfigured by his own calm and gentleness, looking down on me with pity because I had cured him by taking away into my being the horror of his affliction and the evil entity that poisoned his soul so that in his frenzy he had leaped at my throat. And I saw in that moment, back by the sea, by the dark murmuring expanse extending from this country to my own small island and the world of Crete, back not only to the sea but also in this high country of music adrift between the mountain pines that, do what I might, I was destined to receive into my heart the spears of the world's evil. I knew I had done it in the high temple so many hundreds of years back, that it was given to me to absorb into my being the evil and tension that made others sick and, under the beautiful, indifferent moon, I was afraid but in a distant and impersonal way because I knew that there was nothing I could do to avoid it.

I heard Ekko speaking at my side. 'It was the young men healers who were used to taking to themselves the entities that give others convulsions. It was too hard and too disintegrating for the women priestesses. The young men so engaged wore white.'

'And also the priestesses were supposed to be capable of higher things,' I spoke a little bitterly.

'In a way,' she smiled, 'but there was no question of which was better or worse or superior or inferior. The women priestesses had other more complicated destinies. There were other roles to be played by the men.'

Now I was back again wholly in the past and in the high country. You could see through the gaps between the trees the falling away of the country from the plateau on which the temple was perched. The grass, shrill green in the Spring, was interlaced with a diversity of small, starry flowers I had not seen on our island. They were flowers of the mountain and thicker in Spring. After the passing of the first months the hillside was parched with the heat of Summer. Down in the valley was a plantation where the pines were wide-set with, in the middle, a clearing where a theatre converged on an open space, with concentric circles of stone seats rising steeply to the last pines and oaks and to the immensity of blue sky which overtopped their summits. Here I saw a male priest leading a woman not convulsed but in a state of still frenzy, with eyes frozenly open and arms held undeviatingly forwards with hands bent at right-angles and her palms flat outward. It was as if she were resisting an assault and I knew that her lover had attacked her and that, with the priest, she was reliving the horror she had undergone and that, with his guidance, she would perform what she had lived to others around her so that the horror in her heart and the tension in her limbs would be dissipated in acting out the ordeal she had lived. I saw that what the priest did with the woman would be repeated with many priests and many women and that from it there would emerge later a kind of story and that the theatre which, for us who worked there, was a centre of healing would in time become a place of entertainment where people diminished their own pains in witnessing the agonies and released tensions of others.

Now I saw myself lying not in my white robes but with a young priestess dressed in a glowing dark blue, not intensely dark but the colour of the sea in a Summer twilight. 'Blue,' said Ekko, 'was the colour of truth.' I am looking from a narrow cave to where the river emerges from the trees and sweeps in sunlight across the shoulder of the hill and falls by a cascade to a lower level. 'The scene is changed,' I said. 'The young priestess is saying, "Now your thoughts are different. So much of what seems to be thinking is remembering without effort. You remember the last night before you came to the temple? Can you remember the endless high plantations, the hours alone and the straying goats?" '

'I can see all that and the goat herds passing.'

' "It is all coming back without effort. The more you remember the more you will heal because to remember is to go back to the same source which is responsible for healing." '

I held fast to Daria. I knew Daria was the young priestess though she was fair no longer but brown haired, brown eyed with a slow deep voice and easy arms and shoulders. 'Hold fast to her,' said Ekko. 'She was with you the last time. She will be with you at the end in this.'

Then I saw how she was with me the last time. I was writhing again on the floor in the convulsive state of the falling sickness with my lips and cheeks engorged and the froth blown out obscenely from the angles of my mouth and dribbling idiotically down my chin. My eyes moved forwards and the foaming ceased to pour from my lips. It seemed for a moment that I was escaping from the fit but as I lay still the silence continued and it was clear that what I escaped from was life itself. By my side in this life Daria was no longer gripping my hand but stroking it gently. 'The young priest who did this work did not last long,' Ekko said softly in an even voice. 'It was arduous work and many died young.'

'Perhaps I will live longer this time.'

'Perhaps,' said Ekko. At my side I felt Daria shiver. The tremor went from her fingers to my own, and by the shore, in the heat of Summer, I was cold on the mountains in the depth of Winter.

Now we were back in this world and I was mortally tired. I sat on a rock and looked at the sea. Ekko and Daria sat beside me. I was glad that their hands no longer held mine. It took me too far with the touch of their fingers. I was back again in this world and glad to be away from these earlier acts of my destiny which seemed invariably related to the last chapters which concerned me in the book of fate. It seemed I was doomed to suck into my substance so much of the evil of the world for the benefit of others. I sat relieved and happy that the white road of life still stretched a long way before me. I could see the next corner but not beyond it. I looked peacefully at the rocks whitened in the moonlight and listened to the secret of the sea. Its blue, its width and its mystery seemed not separate impressions but part of a single sensation. It was a deep voice speaking to me. The murmur of its waves were soft and persuasive. It spoke of eternity and death and escape from matter. At that moment the sea seemed more real in its voiceless immensity than the land. 'You are back in the world,' said Ekko. 'You are back with your mother in the womb of time.'

We went back slowly through the night, through the forests and the cornland towards Eleusis. In those hours I was indifferent to fatigue and to the past and the future. I was aware as never before of the gold of the corn, molten in the moonlight, of the rolling silver clouds of olive that seemed not only to reflect the moon but to be an insulation from it. I felt all the perfumes of the night and the haunting murmur of the receding sea.

We said goodnight to Ekko when we saw the temple at Eleusis rising spectral in the moonlight and seeming at that moment as much a menace as a blessing. I went with Daria to our lodging and we lay naked together, clinging to each other because of the fear of the past and future which spoke to me through the revelations made to me the previous hours. I had seen my own death in my last life. It was a comfort to know that Daria would be with me at the end in this but I wondered how it would come. The thought was painful because I was young and however much I saw into what was beyond death it was always the fall of a heavy curtain and the shutting away of the small things of life which, built together, made for human happiness however much the Gods call us to greater achievements. My mind was racing with thoughts of the past and future and suddenly I remembered what I had said to Electra that she would be with me at the end. I could not see Daria and Electra together and I consoled myself with the thought that what I had said to the latter was a kind of graceful epithet designed to fill a painful gap in a conversation.

Then all this moving between worlds became too much for me and I was aware of Daria's body naked beside me, not as it had been in the past, something total and entire and which brought me peace, but of something cunningly and intricately constructed, an ecstatic labyrinth of secret fissures, non-touched, non-explored, a whole world beneath my fingers. My hand strayed to her breasts and descended her flanks. I was lying on my side but I moved above her. I saw her eyes shining in the moonlight. They were neither welcoming nor restraining but simply loving. Then the air was pervaded with the scent of broom. It was no longer the season and the flowers had died with the heat of Summer and the dry pods thickened on the switch-like branches. Then I felt the deep stabbing of needles in my lower abdomen and knew for the first time that this was not only the message of her presence – how could it be her presence when she lay beside me – but a deep anodyne for desire, a substitute in my own tissues for the act of love. So all thought of possessing her died in my heart. It passed away from me suddenly, decisively, without any effort. I looked into her eyes and saw behind her head the face of the priestess who had nursed me and taught me high in the mountains five centuries before. I knew it was the priestess who brought back the smell of broom to me and which I had always concluded was the presence of Daria. Now I knew that it was the priestess in blue behind her shoulder and that when she came in the scent of broom she was acting as my guardian angel.

Still holding me the whole length of her body but with no desire in her flesh or mind Daria said softly, 'Now are you happy you came to Eleusis?'

'Yes. It is good and bad but in what I have learnt I have entered a new world.'

'It was better in the other life up in the mountain.'

'How long have you known about our last life together?' I said.

'In the last weeks since we came to Eleusis.'

'When I first saw you coming over the hill on the island I thought of you always as something immediate, as the stab of a spear or a pang of perfume. You seemed so much of the present.'

'So I was,' she said. 'You have awakened something in me. I see now that it was simply that I remembered you from the past. Didn't it seem to you that we had met before?'

'It did not seem anything to me because I did not think about it. I simply spoke to you as though I had known you always.'

'So you have,' she said. 'When I came to Eleusis I found how it had been with us. It was from contact with Ekko.'

'She told you the story?'

'No,' said Daria, 'I remembered in her presence. She confirmed what I saw. It happened as it did with you tonight. Are you sure——'

'Sure of what?' I said.

She did not answer but I knew what she was thinking. She had seen more clearly than I because she was a woman, because she was closer to Ekko and because their perceptions were sharper than mine. I had always thought of Daria and Ekko as close to each other,

96

each, in her own way, concerned to protect the other. It was not strange that I should have had this feeling about Daria. It was inexplicable that I should think this of Ekko. When I had first seen her she had frightened me with her sharp features and the iron scrutiny of her eyes, but now, in a way, I had come to love her and I felt she loved me too. I could not understand her because I had assumed that priestesses and oracles were above and beyond such feelings. 'Was there something you wanted to tell me?' I said.

'Only a little about that other life and how it differed from Eleusis. Up in the mountains there was no question of mirrors or magic. In a way there was no question of training anybody for anything. Of course we helped people to ease their muscles and empty their minds but we only chose for priestesses and healers those born with the gift and almost ready to practise it. What we gave them was the benefit of our experience and what they learnt from being with others made in the same way. It all came slowly. The place itself helped. It was chosen for the purpose. It enabled us to live more fully and to remember more deeply. The two things are the same. What we are taught about the Gods and the immortal psyche came from women who had themselves spoken with and seen the Goddesses and other messengers. It was a question of learning for a few who were specially made and had special experiences. Only a few initiates were added to that number and these because they were born not made. There were no initiation ceremonies such as you have at Eleusis because nobody aimed to increase the number of initiates to more than a handful. You see we were not concerned with the main-tenance of law and order in the community. Those we accepted as priests *lived* law and order. We did not try to convert the sick into anything particular. We did not try to make initiates of them although some were healed because their illnesses were the struggles of their bodies to resist the light. That is the big difference between the past and Eleusis. Eleusis believes that something can be done for a great many by an increasing number of initiates and because of this the world will be a better place. We,' – it was strange how completely she had reverted to her previous life – 'we believed in using the capacities given us to relieve the pains and sicknesses of men and to please the Goddesses and those who wander still unappeased in their pity for the living.'

'Why do you speak all the time of Goddesses not Gods and only of priestesses?'

'Because that is how it was.'

'So there is something lacking in men which is present in women.'

'I am afraid so,' she laughed, 'but the fates are kind. There are men with female souls.'

'Like the monster in the colonnade who will ogle men?'

'No, like you,' she said. 'Female and male are not merely matters of sex but attitudes. The female is always passive.'

'On the island I was recognized as choleric and ill natured.'

'That is your human self. In your psyche you are a woman. You perceive rather than think. You submit rather than struggle. Even when you are irritable you are not aggressive. You are only angry with people who come between you and your destiny.'

We slept very peacefully until long after dawn.

10

NEXT morning it was as though the furies had been loosed. I was walking with Daria down the colonnade when we heard screeches, moans and a higher, discordant whimper like a beast in labour. We walked to the near end of the colonnade that led to the temple. Lying on the ground I saw my obese admirer, the woman's fillet round his forehead disarranged and occluding one eye. The other eye was frozen and congealed like the eye of a dead fish. He lay on his back with his face flattened out until it was more rectangular than circular. It was as if lying on his back emphasized the flaccidity of his toxic tissues. His large jaw sagged, his gaping mouth was both indubitably piscine and idiotically human, and he looked like a mound of flesh in coma. Quite suddenly there issued from this decomposing puddle a harsh, grating shriek. Then, as though responding absurdly to some inaudible summons, the sagging tissues of his body stiffened instantly, his one uncovered eye moved downwards and inwards and after a minute he shook with convulsions.

Around him his entourage bleated but did nothing but raise their hands to heaven. After a few minutes he lapsed again into an inhuman coma that was rather a sleep of tissues than a sickness of man. Then once again I heard the same shriek and saw the same obscenely retracted eye. He went from one fit to another. Nobody did anything. I had hoped the priest Nicetas would arrive. I looked at the monster's servants. They were mostly male and the few females among them looked more masculine than the others. The women had blotches of red on their cheekbones and black round their eyes but they used less perfume. I knelt down beside him with one hand touching his forehead and with the other I parted his eyelids to see how much life and consciousness was left in him. As I did so Daria pushed me aside with such force that I almost fell over. 'Leave him to me,' she said.

'No,' I said harshly, 'this is no case for you.'

'Come away. There is nothing you can do.'

She held the monster's hands. I still pushed her away. After that there was a mixed calamitous sensation of a crack in the earth and a great sound bursting from within my head.

The next thing I remember is lying in the shadow of my lodging with Ekko beside me. 'It is over now. You will never have another illness like this.'

'Was it a bad attack?' I said.

'It was not one attack but a series. Now you must rest.'

'I must know what happened.'

'No, you must rest,' she repeated.

'I cannot rest without knowing.'

'You went from one attack to another. Hush, my child, you must hear no more now, except that never again will you suffer like this.'

'Where is Daria?'

'She is asleep.'

'Why?' I could feel from the heat and the light between the door that this was the hour of the mid-day heat.

'Because she has not left you since yesterday morning. Go back to sleep.'

She put a hand on my forehead. There was a whistling sensation of black shapes and stars seen for a moment with clouds racing past me. Then I fell asleep. When I wakened Daria had returned. 'Tell me what happened,' I said.

'You have been asleep?'

I saw the terror in her eyes. 'Not only asleep,' I said.

'You passed from one convulsion to another.'

'You thought I was going to die.'

'Ekko stayed with you. She held your head between her hands. When the convulsions ceased she was a wizened old woman. Now she is herself again.'

'And you?' I said. It horrified me to think that she, too, may have had convulsions.

'I held your hands. I gave my psyche to you and helped to heal you but Ekko absorbed all the force of evil which pierced you.'

'And he, the monster, how did he fare?'

'His convulsions ceased after you had held him for a matter of moments. He has now left Eleusis. He walked up and down like something inflated. He said he had been initiated into the Mysteries and had also encountered a messenger of the Gods. He meant you. He said he was dying and you cured him of his malady. His servants described you as a kind of God.'

While I was listening to Daria I was thinking hard with that kind of thinking which is not reasoning but which involves the completing of another's thought by one of one's own. 'Was he sick with this malady before he came to Eleusis?'

'I do not think so,' she said. 'He contracted it here.'

'Listen,' I said. 'He not only contracted it here but this place produced it. I have had the falling sickness without convulsions since I was a child. Why should he start at his age – he must be over forty – with one convulsion after another so that if he had continued he would have died of it. I tell you it has to do with Eleusis.'

'I know nothing of his past history.'

'I will ask Ekko.'

When Ekko returned she smiled as she saw me. 'It is gone,' she said. 'It will never come back again. Even the attacks you had before will go. This is because you see more clearly than ever back and forward in time and have no further need of these plunges into what you call unconsciousness in order to see the past and future.'

'Why did *he* get these attacks?' I said abruptly.

'He may have been subject to them.'

'You know as well as I do that this came upon him because of something which happened in this place.'

'He is a man of dissolute life whose brain has been over inflamed and could well have had convulsions.'

'You know the dissolute seem often favoured by the Gods. Come, tell me the truth.' My voice still seemed to be some way off. I was surprised to hear myself speaking so harshly.

'What I tell you must never be repeated to a living soul. He had these attacks because he could not endure the speed and rhythms of the rituals in which he was initiated. He was terrified by the sudden alternation of light and darkness. He saw the darkness as approaching death. When they focused upon him their capacity to induce the timeless state he went back to the birth of his own mother who was a rich courtesan with better taste than himself but entirely without morals. He remembered being born and how his mother was murdered after his birth because all that was required was a child to inherit and his father had outgrown his need of the woman who was better natured than the one he married to preserve his dynasty. This man in his memories was terrified by what he saw. He felt himself on the verge of madness. The Goddesses took pity and intervened on his behalf so that he suffered the lesser affliction of the falling sickness but the sickness was of such intensity that he nearly died of it.'

'Stop, stop,' I cried. 'There is a gap in the darkness of the last two days. The priests did all they could to control him. What did Daria do?'

'She was not called on to do anything.' Ekko spoke as she would to a child and it irritated me to be patronized because I was returned from death.

'Nevertheless I know that Daria was with him.'

Ekko turned to Daria. 'You tell him yourself. I do not think he will suffer.'

'Tell me quickly, quickly,' I said. 'I saw you naked in the temple.'

Daria spoke slowly and calmly again as if to a child but to a child capable of reasoning and of hearing without pain. 'Nicetas came to me and implored my help. He said there was something in which a woman could excel. He promised me that if I succeeded I myself would be initiated immediately. He believed that Antonides could be saved by the love of a virgin. He spoke quickly and persuasively but with dignity. He said that virginity was a force and not a virtue. I said that my virginity would be given only to Milas but when he said that a man's life was at stake I offered myself because I was seeing with the eyes of the woman who comes in the smell of the broom and I knew I was safe and that no sacrifice would be asked of me. So I lay down naked beside him in a side room of the temple and he cried all the more loudly and said that a demon in the form of a woman had had him in her grip, that the demon was his mother and his mother was a whore. He waved me wildly away. I put on my tunic and came back to you in the colonnade. In the meantime they dragged him out and laid him on the ground. It was then you saw him and touched him and healed him.'

I turned to Ekko. 'Did I heal him?' I said.

'You healed him completely by absorbing his evil, which was transmitted by the evil of the ceremony. To tear at the curtains which hide us from the past is always evil. He is certainly cured but while he is near, and while you are here, and because of your youth and what you have suffered, you are still wide open to the force of evil and that is why you must go from here. You must go also because the mob who saw Daria as a saviour when she went naked to this man see her now as a demon and a whore because she failed to cure him.'

'Is Daria in danger?'

'A little, from the mob. You are in far more danger.'

'From whom, from the priests?'

'You are in no danger from the priests. They only wish you would join them. Antonides has gone to Athens and is singing the praises of the new messenger of the Gods.'

'Who is it that threatens me?'

'No living person. I tell you there is a power of evil which moves through the world like a low wind but which rises in certain places until it has the force of a tempest. It picks up the weak and dilapidated like this creature Antonides. You are one of those who cleanse others by permitting the evil transmitted through them or rising in their hearts to flow through you like the tide. You are made to conduct the lightning of the world's evil and to dissipate it in the earth so that it does not harm others. But you yourself can sicken from what you do for others. This is something you must always remember.'

'It seems to me cowardly to go. I am no longer disappointed in Eleusis. I came here seeking something like heaven. I have seen how

102

Heaven and Hell are interwoven and this terrifying lesson is in a way more satisfying. I must stay and learn more.'

'Do you want Daria insulted in the streets?'

'No one dare.'

'A mob dares anything. A religious mob does not need to dare. It goes mad suddenly and there is no need to choose between courage and fear. In three days' time you will recover. What you suffered was a near-fatal convulsive state but people made as you are recover quickly. Antonides is at this moment thinking why in Athens and singing your praises. You must go secretly in three days and you must never say I told you to do so.'

'And you?' I said.

'I go back to Crete.'

'I will see you there?' I said.

'One day, perhaps.'

I found myself saying illogically and urgently, 'But I cannot live without you.'

'You do not need to. You will feel me near you.'

'It is not the same. A voice and a hand have greater reality.'

'No,' she smiled sadly. 'They have a great semblance of reality.'

'But I will see you again?'

'Not see me but feel me near. It is also possible you will hear me.'

'Hear without seeing. How can that be?'

'Wait, wait. You do not know.' Her voice tapered off and she seemed older than she was. There were fissures near her eyes and folds round her cheeks. The collapse of her fine, rather stony features was pathetic and somehow I could not endure it. She seemed ordinary, human and vulnerable and for some strange reason I seemed to weaken with her. At that moment it was as though we were part of each other. I could not understand it at all.

In three days' time we left for the island. Daria and I looked everywhere for Ekko. We could not find her and I said to Daria that it was hard and cold of her to let us leave without her blessing. Then I blamed myself for the harshness of my thoughts and feared acutely that harm had come to her. 'I know she is safe,' Daria persisted. 'I know you will hear from her again.'

'Hear?' I repeated.

'Perhaps see,' she said. I knew I would never see Ekko again.

11

IT was odd that in going back from Eleusis I was very happy. So
was Daria who took her happiness from me. I had gone to Eleusis a
young man who expected the explanation of life to be written in one
place and in one way. I now saw the folly of my hopes. I had
anticipated a kind of fever glow of illumination. To do myself justice
I had never expected a static and continuing happiness. Instead of my
hopes I had endured a great deal of mystification and some agony. I
had learnt for the first time that pain can be educative. I had known
always that we ensure our worst pains in dwelling too long on our
dearest hopes and that to want too much too quickly is itself, if not a
malady, a disastrous unreason. I knew now that there were tortures
that we did not bring upon our own heads, that the pains we suffered
did not necessarily derive from our own littleness, that Achilles
could suffer undeservedly and not only from his pride or the
weakness of his heel. It was not my fault that a flaw in me which was
not a result of vanity had led to my falling sick and my near death
when I had taken the contamination of evil from Antonides. I saw
what I had never seen before, that we ourselves are a battlefield, that
the war in the stars is fought out in our own heart and that in the
light and shadows there was always the interplay of good and evil.

I was happy in an odd way because I knew the hazards of destiny.
What I had learnt gave life more purpose. I knew that we are
purified by many lives on this earth, that there is a continuous
change of messengers and spirits, beginning with those recently
dead, who join us to the Goddesses and through them to the Mother
Goddess and ultimately to something still more remote which I could
not understand and which was perhaps the last mystery. I saw also
that reverence for the Goddesses was wiser than respect for the
Gods, that the former were more constant and not so prone to the
duplicity of the male deities. I was certain that the replacement of
the Goddesses by the Gods, the priestesses by priests was an
adulteration of what had been pure at the beginning, that the
Goddesses and priestesses gave and the Gods and priests too often

took away. I knew that from the feminine source of being we received energy and that with the male we were subjected to power. All this I had learnt by direct contact and experience and not from teachers. I did not care for this new cult in which people of my age sat at the feet of masters and played with ideas. It seemed to me that those so engaged had impoverished senses. Why argue about what you can feel, or theorize about what you can experience?

We landed back on the island a day of late Summer with the breeze already sharpened by the coolness of Autumn. Crossing the sea it was beautiful to see our single mountain rising blue tinted and blurred in the light of dawn to take substance with the coming of the sun so that all that was left of the blue of night were ragged patches of shadow between the rocks towards its summit. It was beautiful to round the foothills of the mountain and to see the first houses, very white and welcoming with the sun risen, their staring white walls outlined more sharply against the sea's blue glitter.

Trouble began when we left the quay and stole not through the port but round the fringes of the town as though we were in alien country. I had feared to see Electra waiting for me at the quay. I knew she was the type who week in week out would meet all the ships. Her devotion to me was something twisted round my heart and brain like the tough, inseparable branches of an evergreen rose. There were times when her affection for me seemed to kill what was left of the feeling I had for her as a young child. At the same time I could not withstand the imploring intensity of her near-black eyes. When she turned them on me she always bombarded me with questions but I knew that deep down what she wanted of me was a deeper, more constant love than I could ever give. She could not accept that it was impossible for me to return to the state of dependence on her which had been mine in my first years when I was happy to accept her as my love, my playmate and above all my mother. To act as my mother had been her favourite game and it was her tragedy that I had grown up beyond it.

I was relieved when we skirted the port without seeing Electra. Had I not had Daria with me I would have been happy to see her. In spite of my love for Daria I felt warmer towards Electra because of my separation from her. 'I think we are safe,' I said to Daria.

Daria only smiled. 'Surely she will be waiting. She will always be waiting.'

'She is not here,' I said.

We went on in silence out of the town up the white streak where the path cut in the pale rock ascended the headland. 'Look up there,' said Daria.

I looked up and saw the small figure curled up in the cushion of turf and thyme on the flat land overlooking the cliff and the tongue of the sea which flicked at the small, arrow-headed bay. 'She has seen us,' said Daria. 'We must go on now.'

I went up beside her with my heart sinking and longing for the freedom and anonymity of the long roads of Greece.

Because of the speed of our ascent and because of her smile Daria seemed almost welcoming when we met Electra. The latter gave a little twitch of recognition from her lips which, normally full, red and loving, were now tight and unnaturally compressed. She did not look at me at all. I went up to her and threw my arms around her. She stood stiffly upright submitting to my embrace. I pressed her close to me. Quite suddenly she urged her body towards me in a paroxysm of longing. Then she looked towards Daria and recognizing the hopelessness of the procedure let fall her hands as though she were relinquishing life itself. 'I am glad you are back,' she quavered.

'There are so many things I have to tell you,' I said.

'I would have thought so.' She thrust her head forward with a sudden reptilian movement as she darted a venomous glance at Daria.

'But there are,' I said feebly. 'I have been away so long. All sorts of things – about the Mysteries, I mean.'

'Yes, the Mysteries,' she said. She had a bunch of wilted flowers in her hands. With great concentration she tried to straighten their stalks. She was filling in time and her heart was broken.

I waited for her to ask me about the Mysteries. She did not utter a word. Daria looked at her with the deep, level stare which I knew so well and which represented pity, the capacity to see deeply and a kind of detachment. Then she spoke slowly. 'You must tell Electra everything that has happened and all we have seen. That will take a long time. You must spend many hours together.'

Electra's mouth twitched back again in a savage reflex of hate and relief. 'Have you many hours to spend?'

'Yes, many, for you.'

I was angry with both of them. 'Now I must go to my father,' I said. I kissed Electra again. This time she let her lips lie on mine but made no attempt to return my kisses. When we left her she raised her right arm in an angular and doll-like gesture and gave me the flowers she had gathered. 'They are to welcome you home,' she said.

As I looked at her tear-smudged face, and the living darkness of her eyes, I knew that in some way I would love her always but not in the way she wanted.

When we got home my father's welcome was a mixture of morbid enthusiasm and creeping doubt. It was obvious that he would have preferred me to return as something tangibly labelled and officially recognized. Perhaps I should have returned as a monument. He would never abandon his idea that I was a son of the Gods and the fact that I could not tell him forthwith that I had been recognized as such filled him with chagrin and a peevish and illogical bitterness. I could read, in his wavering and accusing eyes, the thought that I was a poor return for the care spent on me and the muddled edicts and theories with which he had engulfed me and which passed in his eyes for a sound education.

Daria had at first suggested she would leave that day for her house in the East of the island but I persuaded her without difficulty to stay the night. 'It will be easier for you if I stay,' she said. I was relieved that she did so because I needed some protection against my father. So did she because he devoured her with his eyes and regarded her as his recompense for my not having been accepted as a son of the Gods. As the evening wore on he intoned, in a semi-reverent semi-lascivious chant, 'Beautiful, beautiful,' as he stroked her cheeks. He regarded the ritual use of the word beautiful as an alibi for his explorations which became from time to time a little more intimate. With all the respect I had for my father – there was no other feeling of which I was capable – I felt it too much when he touched her thighs but she bore his explorations with the calm concentration one devotes to the movements of an insect in half a blade of grass. This was one of the mysteries surrounding Daria. In her, chastity was mingled with scientific detachment. Because she was virginal she never blamed others for their animal appetites.

She left early next morning. 'You have to face him some time. It had best be now.'

'I will see you perhaps the day after tomorrow. I will look for you over the hill.'

'No,' she said. 'You must see Electra.'

'But I only said I had much to say to Electra to ease her pain.'

'You were right to say it and must do what you promised.'

'But it is you I love.'

She held both my hands and looked into my eyes. It was a gesture she used when she wished to put something more firmly into my soul. 'I do not want Electra hurt.'

'She hates you,' I said hopefully.

'That is why I do not want her hurt. She hurts herself and enough already by her own hate.'

'What you say is unnatural, that is if you love me.'

'What you feel is all too natural,' she said. 'In some matters we ought to be a little beyond nature.'

She kissed me with the full warmth of her mouth but left me quickly. She went over the hill and away from me. After our months together I was anguished and felt myself wounded. I felt that she was too detached from herself. She said that she loved me but did she truly know how much she meant to me? Also it was hard to comprehend her kind of virginity. She had lain naked beside me and had removed my desire from me. At the same time I felt that had I been insistent she would have responded with ardour. It was also difficult to understand the kind of chastity which was not revolted by the idea of contact with Antonides.

I longed to have Ekko beside me to intercede for me. Though she was a priestess with sometimes a profile of stone to me there was nothing inaccessible and chilly about her. But Ekko was returning to Crete and it seemed that I had seen her for the last time. Certainly it was not far to Crete but suddenly, without real foundation, I felt that the visit to Eleusis had been a disaster. I was suddenly very tired. Without Daria I was very lonely. To be left alone with my incessantly garrulous and constantly probing father only increased my sense of isolation.

We sat in the porch in the morning with the milder sun of the approaching Autumn inserted, in narrow silver sheets, between the columns. 'You tell me you were offered speedy initiation and you refused it. Why?'

'I did not wish to be a priest.'

108

'Again why?'

'I am not interested in government.'

My father threw his hands aside and stared at them for a moment in surprise and then laid them with fabricated self-discipline upon his lap. 'Not interested in the government of the universe? Not interested in the cosmic plan? Not interested in what the Gods are arranging for us?'

'Highly interested, but not in the rule of the Gods on earth.'

'And why not, pray?'

'Because they depend on the priests to maintain discipline.'

'And what wrong can be said of the holy priests?'

'The choice of initiates is bad.'

'Certainly they chose you.' My father tried to smile but only achieved the noise and gesture of a sheep coughing. 'Who else was chosen?'

'A sodden creature who loved both sexes equally and was drenched in perfume.'

'What you tell me is rubbish. He was not chosen for these qualities.'

'No,' I said. 'It was because he was a prince.'

'Exactly,' screamed my father. 'He had been given divine authority by the Gods and it was not for you to question it. Can't you see that his perfume, his love for both sexes were blinds to stimulate you to see the essential purity of his heart. Don't you see that you have failed in the first simple test?' My father raved on, not mad, not even unreasonable according to his lights, but completely intoxicated by his own theories and by his desire that they should be turned in some way to his own profit.

I did not tell him that I had been ill in taking the evil from Antonides. My father was interested in success and not illness. He had been such a failure as a man but naturally he wanted his son to be a God. Neither did I tell him that we lived many times on this earth. I knew he felt that his life, in which he achieved and suffered nothing, had been one long tribulation from which he expected the fabulous reward of an immediate eternity extended beyond eternity. I did not tell him that there is a nameless something beyond all the Gods we can name and imagine. I was sick of his conversation and I could not imagine it would be improved by shrieks of 'blasphemy'. One thing I did divulge and that was that the Goddesses were more

109

our friends than the Gods and that Eleusis had deteriorated with the steady passage into the hands of the male priesthood. I did not speak too philosophically on these matters. I gave what I thought was an appetizing description of the real basic importance of women. I thought, naively I feel, that this would please him. He had had so many women that I felt it only rational that he should count this to his credit. Numbers meant something, after all. I visualized him with the vine leaves awry round his forehead and showering what he called love on those who were unable to respect him. I was totally wrong. It was clear that he thought the purposes of women were limited. He regarded it as adequate reward for them that they should submit to his fumbling ardour. It was only natural that this should classify the Goddesses as below the Gods. Perhaps he saw himself in the next world as exercising his present privileges at the expense of the Goddesses.

When he said he was exhausted he sagged forward with his long, pretentious intellectual face contrasting so strongly with his pendulous sagging and unmuscled abdomen. 'I expected you at least to be a high priest at Eleusis. Or perhaps a great governor in virtue of what you acquired at Eleusis. The best you could hope for is to be some kind of irreverent and blasphemous dealer in herbs like that fool Personides.'

After my return from Eleusis I never argued with or resisted my father. We went our separate ways. He favoured me at times with irrational and pretentious conversation. His meaningful life was lived with female slaves. He spent many nights in the hut of Thekla's mother. It hurt me to wonder whether Thekla herself was by now nourishing his needs that seemed to grow with age and the increasing complexity and fatuity of his opinions. It hurt me to think of Thekla so utilized, in the same way as it hurt me to see birds rising in turmoil when the corn is cut.

Two days after our return from Eleusis I walked up the hill hoping to see Daria coming to me with her arms lifted to embrace me but the hilltop was empty and with it the world and my heart died in me. I waited all day and when she did not come I walked by the wood with an apple green flush in the sky above Crete and over the greenness a frowning cloud. There was beauty and menace in the sky that night. As I went through the wood I saw Thekla walking towards me. She was smiling with all the simplicity of her broad,

110

highly coloured and ardent features. 'Who are you looking for?' I said.

'You want the truth?'

'Yes.'

'For you,' she said.

'Why?'

'Because I love you,' she continued simply.

My mind was so full at that moment with thoughts of Daria that I was dumbfounded that another woman should think she had a place in it. Thekla stood before me, her hands at her sides, not welcoming but waiting, so very much the slave that I wondered why ever she should have told me she loved me. 'You have no right to tell me these things,' I said.

'I know. I am sorry.'

'Why do you do it?'

'You are different from other masters.'

'In what way?'

'There is your illness.'

'You take liberties with me because of my weakness.'

She answered, 'I suppose so.' I do not think she understood fully what I meant. 'Do you——?' She stopped suddenly. She was asking with her guiltless and direct eyes and features if I wanted her body. All of a sudden I was aware of my separation from Daria as pain and hunger. For the most part I felt no desire for Daria. There was in her something which was a substitute for it. But now, in that moment of desperation, I had a scalding sensation in the pit of my stomach and my longing for Daria was a pain beyond my own heart, something elemental like the winds of Autumn. 'Go home,' I said to Thekla. 'Go home, I do not need you.' I was angry with myself because I wanted her so badly and most of all because I had thought of her, if only for a moment, on a lower plane but as a substitute for Daria.

Thekla went off home erect and sturdy with her head held high. She kicked a pebble up the path by way of diversion. She accepted without bitterness that she was little more than a chattel. Perhaps she had thought to elevate herself a little by offering herself willingly. It hurt me that I might have added to her degradation. All of a sudden, quite illogically, I wished I could provide a better home for her.

Next day I awoke as never before with a great tumult in my heart and with a leaden weight in my solar plexus. It was as though the pit of my stomach had become metallic and that its substance vibrated all the more to the agonies I felt. I could not go a day longer without seeing Daria. I called to her to come to me. I sat up suddenly, my nostrils widening, hoping to smell again the perfume of broom which accompanied her when she came to me out of her body. There was no smell but that of night in the room, and the salt of the sea diluting the odour of the aromatic shrubs.

I started early on my journey to the town she lived in on the East side of the island. There was already a touch of Autumn in the air and with the mist from the sea the minutely clanging leaves of the olives were grey and green, without the mysterious filaments of silver with which they were threaded when the sun was shining. I crossed the island through the breath of morning and the heat of noon and came to the forest which overhung the town. Going through the half shade of the forest I was aware of a cloud descending darker than the shadow cast by the upward pointing bunches of pine needles on the tawny branches. 'She will not be here,' I said. Then I had an all-possessing assurance of happiness because I knew that when I thought 'She will not be here', it was to placate the jealousy of the Gods and that in fact I would see her soon with her lifted hands and always those luminous eyes that were still loving even though they saw through me and well beyond me. But when I came to her house I was told by the woman who was head of her slaves that she had gone from the island and would be away for the space of two moons. In the pitiless sunshine the ground seemed to move from under my feet. I reeled with the desolation that emptied the blood from my heart. I marvelled that a few words from a commonplace pretty woman could darken my brain and blind my eyes to the sun. The woman stood watching me with a slight smile and, in the darkness and misery, I fancied she found pleasure in seeing me suffer. Then she handed me sprays of rosemary and myrtle. They were tied together with fine golden thread. As she gave me the flowers she said, 'My mistress says she will return. She asks you not to forget her.'

'What made her go?'

'She has affairs in Crete.'

'Why didn't she tell me?'

'I do not know.'

I tucked the flowers in the fold of my tunic and turned abruptly away.

The way back was a voyage through darkness. Each incident was an eternity yet there were moments when I sank exhausted on the grass when I had no knowledge of what had gone before. What should have been an interminable succession of incidents was a blank. Sometimes when I sank on the grass with the emptiness behind me I wondered if I had died and if I were wandering in the first fields of the next world before the nearest of the spirits had stretched her hands towards me. I felt that perhaps I had had an unusually prolonged attack but when I came to full consciousness of myself I had no throbbing awareness of the world about me and no feeling that its outlines were abnormally sharp. Neither was my right hand raised as at the end of my attacks. It was too soon after my return from Eleusis to realize that I had finished for good with my malady.

The last hours of my journey were dragged out because at least I was moving and this gave me the semblance of purpose. I dreaded the static conception of a home, of being shut up within four walls with the constant rivulet of my father's conversation tugging inanely at its foundations. I walked in the darkness of the moonless night but the stars were low above the treetops and the path through the forest was an opalescent thread. Then I came to the last hill above my home. I walked to its summit on the far side and saw the white porch of our house below and my heart within me seemed to stop altogether and I longed for death or a sleep without hope. It was not just that Daria had parted from me without warning. It was not just that I recognized her as my second self and sharing my psyche. It was as if she had used me cruelly. To have left me without warning was like amputating a limb.

On the very summit of the hill, by the two flat stones where Daria and I had sat together, I smelt broom. A candle was lit in my heart and its flame shot upwards. The clouds dispersed in my brain when I heard the patter of feet coming towards me. I opened my arms. At first all I saw was the pallor of her face and then dark hair and I knew that I was embracing Electra, who was pressing herself to me and sobbing convulsively. I made no attempt to hide the misery I felt. 'It is you,' I said.

'Yes, it is me.' As she said it the incandescent darkness of her eyes

113

was veiled and she knew, deep down and for always, that she was defeated, that in whatever way I loved her it was not with the total spontaneous self-devouring love I had for Daria.

'How did you know you would find me here?'

'By a dream last night.'

I did not wish to hear of her dreams. My fingers clawed at my tunic. I felt a resistance in its folds and touched the rosemary and myrtle Daria had plucked for me. I knew in that moment that it was she who had sent Electra to me. It was she who had given her the dream. It made me feel no better towards either Daria or Electra. I could not escape from the thought that the former had deserted me cruelly and that, to provide Electra as a bandage for my wound, was a crude artifice and that in employing it she was being heartless to both of us. 'But why did you meet me?' I said.

I felt her lithe, half masculine body crumble in my arms. She did not withdraw from me but laid her body long against mine without ardour or warmth, as though all that she hoped for was physical support. 'I knew you would be unhappy,' she said listlessly.

'How?'

'They told me in the dream.'

'Who?'

'I don't know.' She was not like my father who attributed such a message to the Gods.

'It was kind of you to come.'

'Kind?' She spoke softly but spat the word out sharply, hatingly as though it had been acid. 'You have been to see her.'

'She has gone to Crete.'

'I am glad.' Once more her voice in the darkness was the hiss of a serpent. 'I am glad for your sake that you have lost a creature who is beautiful and mindless and a kind of temptress.'

I did not answer. I was beyond exhaustion and at that moment I half shared her opinions.

'I am telling you the truth for your own sake,' Electra continued. In one way or another she had done this for years. 'I have nothing to lose because I know you don't love me.'

'Why do you tell me all this?'

'Because I love you and you are an imbecile.'

Suddenly it came to me that with all her beauty she would never marry and never be loved and would die a virgin. A person without

114

prejudice could say she was more beautiful than Daria. Her features were more patrician and the glowing darkness of her eyes was in itself one of the higher mysteries. She was cleverer and better versed in poetry than any man I knew. She had loved me almost since I could walk but the fates had ensured that I was given to another. It happened that morning when Daria came over the hill and from that moment she represented for me the sun and light whereas Electra, for all her rebellious tenderness, was darkness and mystery and the daughter of the moon. Suddenly the tragedy of Electra's situation struck me with the force of a hammer. She had beauty, she had ability which might ripen one day into something like wisdom. She was loving and loyal and had the power of chastity which goes with unexploited beauty. In spite of all this she would die frustrated. 'Listen, Electra.' I sat down on one of the flat stones and took her in my arms. 'Lay your head on my shoulder.' She did as she was bid and for a moment a pathetic flake of hope lightened the darkness of her marvellous eyes. 'There is no one like you and I will always love you.' The light went out of her eyes. She had heard this before and had tired of it. 'I will always love you——' I had repeated the self-same words so often before. Neither she nor I could bear this further repetition. All I saw at that moment was the beauty of her face. All I knew was the emptiness in my own heart, the challenge of her invulnerable chastity and the fire lit in the darkness of my tissues by the slave girl Thekla. When I laid my hand on Electra's breast I swear it was more in tenderness than passion but as her breast hardened in my hand from the shock of surprise I drew her to me and pressed my body to hers.

Her voice was softer than ever and still more venomous. 'Let me go,' she said. 'I did not know you were bestial.'

'But what have I done?'

'I said you were bestial. You would not understand an explanation.'

She rose quickly and ran down the hill. 'Where are you going?' I cried.

She did not answer. I ran after her and caught her and she struggled in my arms. 'Let me go,' she cried. She bit my fingers and kicked my feet.

'I cannot let you go. You must stay here tonight.'

'I am finished with you, finished.' She ran off into the wood. I followed her and there was the same biting and scratching with the same dry, hopeless and agonizing sobs.

I let her go. As I could not love her I had lost even the right to fight with her.

In the days following I lived a dumb misery in which time and place were blurred and where only the succession of night and day were significant. I thought myself ill because I had little idea of the reality of suffering in love. I had seen people whose lovers had died and who had wandered the woods sensible of a great emptiness, of hands withdrawn and of voices silent. I had heard the wailing of women for their children, but this had seemed to me always an inevitable and painful state and in some ways detached from the course of life, as though a healthy man had fallen and broken a leg and found that his actions and interests were impeded by it. I was unprepared for what I felt in these days and which went deep into my heart. The fact that I was so paralysed of thought and action made me all the more resentful of Daria. This, and the fact that I was goaded by loneliness, drove me to the port to make my peace with Electra. This was not as I had thought. As soon as she saw me she began to weep. She looked beautiful when she wept. I thought that in those moments she was more beautiful than Daria. It occurred to me later that perhaps her suffering made her more lovely but I did not dwell on an idea which seemed to be irrational and morbid, perhaps a little like the ideas she held herself.

She took me inside her house and held me by the hands, looking at me with her eyes not intent like Daria's but constantly darkening as though she could not report the intensity of her own love. Squeezing my hands lightly, she begged me never to touch her again as I had done last evening. 'It stirs something within me I cannot support.' I wondered when she said it if she had ambitions to be a priestess. Her face resembled that of Ekko in the sharpness of its features. The resemblance ended there because Electra's face was incessantly mobile and there was nothing stony about it. Then she added, 'I love you more than I ever have done.' The thought came into my head that her love had intensified with the disappearance of Daria. She was living her life in the other's absence. This was something I could well understand.

We went up the headland away from her widowed mother who was a stately uncomprehending person from whom Electra inherited

116

the dignity of her features and the slim, hard grace of her body but who did not share her interests and was frightened of her daughter's probing curiosity about things living and dead. There, above the sea, we talked of Eleusis. It surprised and relieved me that Electra preferred this subject to the state of our relations with each other. I did not speak of Antonides because her face stiffened when one spoke of the body. It was strange that she wore always the full tunic which covered the breasts and which was only worn by the older among the free women on our island. Neither did I speak of all I had found wanting at Eleusis. I knew that she lived, like a solitary bird on the island searching alone for what she thought the truth. I did not wish to sadden her by telling her that some of those who thought as she did were contaminated. I spoke only of the truths I had heard and not of those responsible for their utilization. 'Did you know that we live again and again on this earth?' I said.

'I have often thought it possible. I see the same places in dreams and sometimes the same faces. It seems to me sometimes that I am more alive asleep than waking.'

'That is because your brain is still and your heart hears better.'

She frowned a little. She set great store on what she thought. I sometimes wondered if she thought like a man, if, in fact, there was something of a man in her body. I looked at her slim, hard-muscled thighs. Nevertheless all she wished to be to me was a kind of mother. 'It is necessary to be sceptical in order to believe,' she said. 'Those who are not sceptical at first are not to be trusted with the truth.' I thought this was intelligent but I did not tell her so because I thought she would continue in the same vein. 'The colours I see in my dreams,' she continued, 'are more real than what I see now while I talk to you.'

'That there are many lives is not what is taught to the people.'

Electra tossed her head. 'They only teach the people what they are fit to know. There are other truths——' She paused and looked away. She was imploring me with her heart to tell her all I had learnt at Eleusis. She was far too proud to ask me directly.

'In the early days there were more priestesses than priests.'

'No, is it true?' She was breathing heavily. 'Who told you this?'

'A priestess call Ekko. Also I saw it myself.'

'You went back to the past.' She clutched my hand.

'Back to the days when there were no priests but only women and when only the Goddesses were worshipped. The Gods were seen for what they were, deceitful male figures still practising the aggressions and lies that had helped them in this world.'

Her hard fingers were biting in my palm and she cried, 'Go on.'

'And beyond the Goddess was a supreme Goddess, a kind of mother of the earth and of the moon and stars and a mother of the other Goddesses and of all things living.'

What she said next surprised me. 'The sun, too, is a woman. The story of Apollo as a sun God is nonsense. How could a man have the warmth of the sun?'

"I have always thought that Apollo was a man like the rest of us and that they magnified his exploits in legend.'

'This Mother Goddess you talk about is a true Goddess. She has no earthly origins.' Electra was talking low and intently and for once in her life she was unaware of my presence. It was a tribute to the intensity of her belief. 'This Mother Goddess has created all things.'

'What about the evil in the world?'

'It came from the interference of the Gods,' she said vehemently. 'They were right at Eleusis, the Gods are bad. A few have good qualities but most are bad.'

I did not ask her why, if they were bad, the Mother Goddess permitted them to exist. Had I done so there would have been an unending tangle of argument. Also I wished her to retain all the comforts she could get from the idea that the Mother Goddess was supreme. I thought it would help if I said, 'Beyond the Mother Goddess there is something which is still more wonderful and nameless, not a woman in essence but feminine in tendency,' but Electra would have none of it and cried sharply and conclusively, 'There is nothing beyond the Mother Goddess.' Then she seized my hand and pressed it to her breast without discomposure and with a serenity I had never seen before in her dark eyes. I smiled to think that she did instinctively and happily what had repelled her when I myself had made the same gesture. I understood from that moment that her love of me was part of her cult of the Mother Goddess. She had loved me as a child in our first years. I was still her child. I was probably the only male she could tolerate. She looked so happy with my hand on her heart that I schooled myself to let her be my mother.

'Will you take me to Eleusis?' She threw the question at me swiftly, aggressively, as a man casts a spear.

118

'One day.'

'You went with *her*.' Now the words poured out volcanically. There was fire and acid and the hiss of steam. 'This girl you went with was beautiful and animal, without mind or heart. It is an odd thing that she did not corrupt you. It is the blessing of the Gods, of the Mother Goddess, that she has left you.'

It was on the tip of my tongue to say that it was Daria who had sent her to me in what Electra thought a dream and that without Daria she would not have met me in the dark hours when I stumbled back empty from Daria's home. 'I will take you one day,' I said. It occurred to me that if I lived a long time the journey would become progressively easier with age.

'You tell me you saw into the past,' said Electra.

'Into a past life beyond Eleusis and over the mountains.'

'What were you doing in this life?'

'I was healing the sick.'

'Were you a priest?'

'There were no priests. I was a kind of assistant to the priestesses.'

Electra's eyes glowed. I could see that she regarded this as an ideal situation. She would be a priestess and I would learn from her. 'You must go back to Eleusis immediately.'

I cried out sharply, 'No'. The beauty of the journey with Daria was still fresh in my heart. Now that this was a memory I had to inter the thought of retracing my steps along the long road which, without Daria, was unbearable to me.

'You cannot throw away your talents. You must be trained.'

'Not yet,' I said. 'I have not yet absorbed all I found at Eleusis.'

'Not to return would be an insult to the Mother Goddess. We will go back in the Spring.' When Electra spoke like that I do not think she had any desire to dominate me harshly. She was injecting into herself a confidence she did not feel. 'In the Winter we can meditate about these things. We could go to Crete in the Winter and read the manuscripts there.'

Though I could see the island from where I sat the name Crete was an invisible wound from which I bled freely. Daria was in Crete. Suddenly I felt that I had wronged her, that to me she was as lovely as ever in nature as in looks. I wished to confess to someone the hate I had had for her. There was nobody to confess to but Ekko.

My adoptive mother, now curled up closely beside me, was consumed with hate for Daria. I longed for Ekko, for her clear thoughts, her eloquent silences and her sudden outrageous bursts of humour. I thought how Ekko was herself in Crete. It never occurred to me that she and Daria might meet. Still less did I consider that they might be drawn together by the spindles of destiny. Least of all did I think they would meet by intention.

I got up abruptly and said goodbye to Electra. 'Why are you going?' she asked.

'There are so many things to think of.'

'There is one thing only, to develop your gifts. You have seen into other worlds. You must go on looking.'

'And of course you must help me.' At that moment a little of the acid in her nature had spilt over to me.

'With all my heart,' she said. When she was set on any course of action Electra was totally devoid of humour. She persuaded herself that all her actions were dedicated to the search for truth and that all the paths she took were consistently unerring. In the face of this attitude there was no room in herself or others for any trace of humour.

12

WITH the coming of Autumn the rains were heavy. There was no fleeting saturation of the parched earth and after that cool, crystalline mornings with the sun's silver feathers on the dancing sea. With the advent of October the sun receded. There were long sullen days when the clouds were low. The mist hung heavy in the valleys in the mornings. Behind the mist was the moaning sea. It was more like Autumn in another country. When, with November, the trees dripped greyly in the mornings with the lingering rain, my heart, now closed to Daria and the long grey days, woke to life on a sudden in a cry of protest for the absent light. I could not see the sea from the hill beside the house. I could hear the clatter of its waves against the rocks and the unseen menace of its long grey swell.

It was now more than two months since I went to Daria's house. I told myself that never again would I repeat that journey. Sometimes when my thoughts drifted I saw her return across the hilltop and always her hands were lifted towards me. But for the most part I excluded her from my mind and she never called me back with the smell of broom and the queer, dancing tension which announced her presence. But on one of the first days of Winter, with a thick blanket of cloud weighed down and sinking further with its weight of moisture, I went back to her house instinctively as a man trapped in a labyrinth moves to the light at the end of the tunnel. She was not there and there had been no message from her. The genteel and vindictive woman left in charge of the house had no suggestions as to when she would return. Going back home from Daria's house was not so agonizing as my first return. It was now bearable because of the anger roused within me by my self-contempt. I saw no further point in indulging in these agonies.

When I returned home that night the wind had dropped and the night was opaque and airless. Suddenly, avidly, I thought of Thekla. I longed to find her in the wood but that night there was neither moon nor stars and Thekla, like most of her kind, felt the menace of the dark hours and was probably at home. I went into the hut where she lived with her mother. I had no eyes at all for the latter. My blood was aflame and I sat staring at Thekla. The smile she gave me was grudging and brief. She could not help smiling with her wide-set, candid eyes but her mouth moved little and she looked at her mother. I entered with my mouth dry, my heart ticking wildly and my blood boiling for Thekla. I paid little attention to her mother though I noticed that the oily greeting she smeared over her face when she saw me was briefer than usual and that, while I stared hungrily at Thekla, her mother's great head was swivelled towards me as though someone had moved the head and shoulders of a demon in stone. I knew she was defending her daughter from me. I knew this could mean one thing only, that recently Thekla had attracted more attention from my father and her devoted mother would ensure that her child's virginity was sacrificed to the most profitable employer. Of course I could have defied her mother and taken Thekla back with me to my room, but suddenly I was nauseated, not by my desires or by her mother's presence, but by the inharmonious futility of my life. I left them without a word and went to my couch and tossed all night thinking not of Daria or Thekla but only of Electra, counting it as an immense merit that she loved me, seeing again the beauty of her face and the hard, leathery elegance of her boy's body and wondering why she did not excite me more.

After that night I spent my days in the company of Electra. The weather cleared, we were even unafflicted by the winds of Winter. The sea was calm, a sheet of beaten silver and the ships sailed between us and the shores of Crete. When we sat on the headland or walked sometimes by the shore where the oracle had perished there was one subject only which interested Electra. This was the matter of my spiritual development. I had made a great error in speaking to her of my glimpse into the past. Now I erred still further. It was difficult to do otherwise. She was softened and unspeakably gentle because I accepted her love for me. I no longer found it irritating and wished there was something I could do to inject into my feelings for Electra a little of what I felt for Thekla. Daria had faded from my mind. Softened by Electra's presence and her changed attitude, and aware of my dependence on her, I told her one day of how Antonides had been cured of his stream of convulsions after I had touched him. Her eyes shone and leaning over me she kissed me for the first time slowly and lingeringly on my lips. Her kiss was inexpressibly tender but devoid of passion. I felt no desire but it opened by heart because I felt that this was the summit of our intimacy. It was all she would ever get.

She stroked my hair and said, 'Perhaps, my love, you are a great healer. You have often foretold the future. Now you have seen into the past. These things must be developed. Let us go with the Spring to Eleusis.'

'What would happen to you if I became a priest?'

'I would try to be a priestess.'

'Can you see into the future?'

'A little, in dreams. I have no gifts, only the desire to learn.'

I did not argue with her. There was nothing I wanted to learn. There was much I had wished to experience before Daria left me. Now the light had gone out and for me there were no consolations in what Electra called philosophy. But when she returned to the question of healing this was something different. I looked at my hands. Some power residing within them or transmitted through them had cured a man who would have died without me. That at least was something to do. When Electra said, 'You are luckier than I. You were born with these gifts,' something wakened in me. I was no longer interested in seeing the past. I wondered if the gift in my fingers could lift me out of my vegetable torpor.

Suddenly Electra swung round her whole body towards me. It always seemed necessary to her to express an idea by physical movement. 'I think you should go and see Personides. He is a man of experience and has been to Eleusis.'

So one day I made again the journey past the inlet where the tumult of the sea died in the still lake with the water lilies at its far end and where, in the moonlight, I had seen Artemis. I visited him alone and unwillingly because of his previous insolence to my father. I recognized that the latter was an irritant to anyone with a morsel of intelligence but I thought one needed the alibi of blood relationship to have the right to insult him. I put my questions to Personides listlessly. 'You have come under compulsion,' he said. 'I suppose Electra sent you and you did it to please her.'

'Yes.' I spoke passively and without resentment. I had no wish to waste too much emotion on him.

'What is it you wanted to know?'

'If I have the gift of healing.'

'It is written in your hands, in your voice and in your stars. What have you done to make you raise this question?'

I told him the story of Antonides. 'Why didn't they keep you at Eleusis?'

'They tried to.'

'Why didn't you stay?'

'I was looking for the truth. What they live is not the truth.'

'Why?'

'They initiate people who are unfit to be received, who are made sick or evil by being taken back to the past too quickly when all they can do is to live badly in the present.'

'Oh, of course. Some of the worst rulers and governors have been made mad by initiations for which they weren't fitted.'

'It is evil,' I said.

'The world must continue and men must be governed. To have been initiated gives a man authority.'

'Any kind of man?'

'Oh come,' he said. 'You know it is corrupt as well as I do.' He

123

screwed up his half-smiling, half-sneering, ironic mouth. 'The whole world is corrupt. The corruption extends beyond the limits of this world into the universe itself. But they still know something at Eleusis. I have been there myself.'

'What did you learn?'

'What I knew already, in fact, the same as you.' I looked at him slowly, wonderingly and said nothing. 'You were about to add,' he said bitterly, ' "and this is what you have come to".'

I did not respond. 'What would you advise me?' I said.

He half opened his mouth, his sharp jaw fell, he seemed tired and old and at a loss for a word. 'Stay here and replace me. I heal, I advise and I prophesy a little.'

I reflected savagely that this man had once told me I was a son of the Gods. 'Are you happy?' I said.

He smiled bitterly. 'That is not one of my gifts,' he added suddenly. 'Men are very vulnerable.'

'To what?'

'To the power of evil.'

'I am no worse than any other,' I said.

'You are better. That is why you are more vulnerable.'

'You talk in riddles.'

He looked at me intently, contemptuously. 'You know exactly what I mean. You healed Antonides because of your capacity to take to yourself the evil of others.'

'Is this an evil thing to do?'

'Not evil, noble, that is if you have an adolescent flair for nobility. I am doing my duty, I am giving you a warning. The best you can do is to stay here with me.'

Once again I recalled that he had indicated to me that something of the Gods had gone into my substance. Had I, then, so deteriorated that I was reduced to a life as his assistant. 'I shall find something better.' I made no attempt to hide my contempt.

'Come back if you can't.'

As I walked away he called to me softly, 'Beware of Electra.'

'That is shameful,' I said. 'She is loving and helpful.'

'To whom?'

'To me.'

'Loving to you and helpful to herself.'

As soon as I had left him I had no hate for him. I knew he was

124

surgically honest and ageing. He had seen too much and had no close friends.

But though I had no hate for him I felt bereft of all hope by my visit to him. I could not see why he had taken such pains to deflate my hopes. He had said I could heal and had done his best to persuade me to limit my powers.

The rest of the Winter was a grey, eventless misery. I saw Electra constantly and heard nothing but exhortations that I should return to Eleusis and train for a great destiny. I think a good deal of my depression was due to the fact that the world was brooding. No one in the island remembered such a Winter. It rained for weeks and there were floods in the hollows. Then one morning the cap of cloud was lifted from the mountain. In its place there were threads of mist drawn up to and melting in the blue Spring sky. Then once again was the white miraculous snowfall of the almonds in blossom. With the white Spring came the season of the Dionysian rites. I had held them in great contempt because they acted as such an unnatural stimulant for my father. Now this year, because I had lived so many empty months, there was fever in my blood and I felt that I, too, would take part in the revels. My flesh was quickened by the long hours I spent with Electra knowing that, if I lived to be a hundred, she would never be mine. I felt that if she relented she would offer herself as a human sacrifice.

With the approach of the season of Dionysius Thekla's manner changed. She was no longer spontaneous. It was unthinkable that once she had told me she loved me and asked me to take her. Her mother seemed bigger and more bloated than ever. Her face was that of an inflated toad. She waited the festivities with a tittering anticipation in which she hid from the admission of her own repulsiveness. She was emetically servile to my father. Often when she spoke with him she took Thekla with her. Thekla smiled dutifully in my father's presence. She knew the role intended for her by her mother. It was part of her lot to be contaminated. She had too much sense to resent it much. I knew that Thekla was being stored up as a special prize for the Dionysian season. This was only to be expected in view of my father's devout nature. Things had to be done for the prescribed ritual. Thekla had to be deflowered in Spring. When he saw her my father broke into scraps of harsh, discordant music. If he saw that I listened he asked me sarcastically if I was suitably occupied. I could not see how this could be expected of me. He himself had done nothing in life except reverence his own self-indulgence.

I made no plot to forestall my father. When I saw him with the vine leaves in his hair, the flagon in his hand, self-consciously ready for his unnatural obeisance to the forces of nature, he seemed so ludicrous a figure that for me he contaminated the whole festival. I left the house and walked to the left down the slope to the spring. There was no one about. The singing and laughter were still confined to the houses. The moon was high and, though the air was still in the wood and the hollow, the clouds high in the sky raced over the moon and the stars seemed to rock with an invisible current. My body felt light and my feet seemed scarcely to touch the ground. I had drunk no wine. I had left that to my father and to other serious adherents of the ancient Gods.

Then I saw the figure of a girl moving out from the trees. She went to the spring at the foot of the slope and splashed water with her hands on her face and hair. When I came nearer I saw by the roundness of the head, the width of her brow and the broad-set eyes that this was Thekla. She was dressed in white as if for a wedding. I stole up behind her and seized her shoulders. She swung round quickly. Her face in the moonlight was chalky with terror. I could not imagine how such a natural animal as Thekla should be terrified by the touch of a man's arms. When she saw me the terror passed from her face. Tears leapt from her eyes and joined with the water which spangled her face. 'Why did you splash your face in the spring?' I said.

'I wanted to be clean. Will you take me away?'

'Away?'

'Only into the wood and away from the others.'

'Once you loved me and now it is only to escape the others.'

She went down on her knees and kissed my hands fervently. 'Please keep me from the others.'

'You mean from my father?'

'From your father especially.' She shuddered from head to foot.

We went into the wood and lay together on the moss between the trees. Her breast hardened and rose and I felt all the curves of her body to be swollen. She folded her hands behind my neck and drew me towards her until our lips were meeting. Then there was a

126

frenzy so extreme that I was aware only of being buried within her. I did not know she was mine until she lay exhausted with her hands thrown out sideways on the moss beneath us. Then, without speaking, we lay quietly together. We saw the moon through the boughs above us and the streamers of cloud extended by the night wind. Then, shyly, she drew me again towards her. 'Love me as much as you can,' she said. 'I am yours by right. One day you will own me. I want no other master.'

'Is that love?' I said.

'Yes, to me.'

Once again I lost myself in Thekla. I had known no other woman and it seemed to me incredible that anyone so inexperienced as myself should have been so transported by my first adventure. I did not allow sufficiently for the infinite and endless capacity for passion which resided in Thekla. She, too, had given herself to no other but something like a mounting storm inside her had gathered in the days of the white Spring and had burst suddenly and flooded the darkness of my tissues. So when she came to me again I turned towards her, hoping for more intimate pleasure. Then suddenly through the night, earlier than its season, coming from no living plant, I smelt the perfume of broom. I was stabbed with such a recollection of Daria that I drew back from Thekla as though she were infected. I saw the unbitter, animal supplication in her eyes and was unmoved by it. Then her features blurred and I saw in their place the face of Daria, dark eyes replaced by others blue as the deeper waters of the sea, a mist of dark hair dispersed by golden cascades that fell to her shoulders. Then I saw clearly and in detail the face and neck of Daria. Thekla smiled again, brilliantly, happily with her dark eyes. I saw her lips move and the voice which spoke through her was not her own. The accents were clearly Daria's. 'I am come back, my darling. Ask me no more questions. It is time to love.'

I saw Thekla's arms widen but the winged freedom of their movement was certainly Daria's. When Thekla's thighs parted I saw not the dusky brown of her own flesh but the light golden burnish of Daria's limbs. 'Forget everything,' the voice said. 'Think only of me. I am Daria come back. Thekla knows nothing of our love, my darling. Give yourself to me. I am in her body.'

Then there was nothing but the deep breathing silence of the wood unswept by the night wind, and knowing there was nothing but death and love, that love itself was a death, that Thekla was asleep, obliterated for a time, in the psyche of Daria. Then there was no longer the body of Thekla and the voice of Daria but a face more oval and serene than that of Daria with a blue ribbon round an unlined forehead like incandescent snow and, in the centre of the ribbon, a clear-cut diamond with the piercing translucence of streams born in snow. I knew that I saw Artemis as I had seen her naked in the inlet of water lilies. I remembered how she had bathed in the lake and thrown off the water from her body in a thousand crystals. I remembered how Thekla had splashed the water from the spring on her face and shoulders and I knew that there was a living current which joined Thekla through Daria to the Goddess and that I was the convulsed filament which joined them together.

I cannot tell the joys of this second lovemaking because while there was the same sense of being buried within the woman beneath me there was nevertheless no longer the feeling of being dead within her. She had taken me into her body but what had entered into her and been diffused through her by the intensity of our mutual passion was, at the same time, hovering above the trees in the void of the sky and in the space between the stars. A voice inside me was saying, 'It is Thekla and Daria and the Goddess herself,' and with this there was a great ecstasy which, when it died, left me weeping and wandering through a great gap in time so that when I returned I was sitting on the moss with Thekla sitting upright beside me, her face thrust close to mine and her candid dog's eyes searching my own for a little recognition and a little gratitude. 'I am your slave,' she said. 'Your slave and your woman because I gave myself to you. Also I love you. Can you pardon me my love?'

There was no abasement in her manner but a statement of fact. Had she not given her virginity to me it would have fallen to my father. At that moment, in a strange ecstasy which was not composed solely of happiness but involved a greater awareness, I felt my present joy and the future menace. I knew she was my father's by right and that he would assert his authority. But at that moment it seemed not to matter. Thekla's love had enveloped me like a cloak and excluded me from the world's wild weather. Daria was returned and the Goddess had loved me. This was how it separated itself out in something almost discarded which I called my mind, but what I was aware of, in a radiant zone which seemed projected a little outside my body, was that the Goddess Artemis had come to the forest and taken possession of the girl who loved me. It did not mattter if I thought of the girl as Thekla and Daria. The voice which called my body to Thekla's, the heart which had poured into the limbs of Thekla the gift of frenzy, was certainly Daria's. But replacing Daria I saw Artemis the Huntress. She moved through the night and her touch was healing. She had led me out of the trough of depression. When I was young they had said I was a child of the Gods. Now, loved by the Goddess, I could only believe it.

I sat with Thekla until the stars went out.

13

MANY nights after I lay with Thekla, always in the forest and away from the world. I never saw Artemis again. It was the time of the festival and my father's slow frenzy burst one night. He screeched at me that I had usurped his rights and in so doing desecrated a sacred festival. I had withdrawn from it a girl whose best fate was to lose her virginity with the blessing of Dionysius. He had regarded her defloration as his principal religious duty. He rose from his bench and went towards the door. 'I will have her now. Otherwise she will be turned out of the house immediately.'

'You will not touch her,' I said. I looked at him with one vine leaf hanging over the tip of his nose and rising and falling with the rhythm of his breathing. He looked a preposterous clown.

'I will throw you out with her. I have the right.'

'Have you the courage?' I said.

'By the Gods, I have.' He yelled so hard that his headdress fell off. I left him to boil from his unassuaged lusts.

It was well enough that I spent each night in Thekla's company. What I forgot was that day exists as well as night and that the desires of men are not limited to the religious festivals. One day my father came to me as I sat in the porch thinking not of Thekla but of Daria. 'I have asserted my rights,' he said.

At first I did not understand what he meant. He had always seemed to me so incapable of asserting anything that I regarded his words as the irrelevant babbling of one addicted to fantasy. 'I am surprised that it does not concern you,' he continued.

Looking at his deliberately assumed leer – he was not an evil man, he was just potentially worse, that is to say a cipher – I felt that this expression was a signpost pointing to Thekla. 'You have taken Thekla,' I said.

'Yes, this morning, with her full co-operation.'

I went out without saying a word. I was cool and utterly without definable emotion. I was still living in the atmosphere induced in me by Daria and Artemis. I went to the hut in which Thekla lived with her mother. I ordered the latter out of the hut. She looked at me incredulously because she was not accustomed to such treatment from me. She went out heaving, panting and enormous like a stranded whale.

'My father has taken you,' I said to Thekla.

'Yes.' She was in no way agonized. 'I did not like it because I love you but I know he has the right.'

'Let me see your hands.'

I saw the wondering humility in her eyes as she held out her hands towards me. She had the broad hand and the strong blunt fingers of a country slave. 'One day you will be mine,' I said. I meant that when my father died I would inherit her and be an easy master. Her eyes were moist with gratitude. She rubbed her body against me like a cat.

Day and night after that first night with Thekla in the forest I thought of Daria. I felt convinced she would come again. Surely she would return to me in the heart of the white Spring. Day followed night and I could not understand her absence. It was odd that I did not feel a greater sense of deprivation. Something of my experience with the Goddess Artemis had been built into the core of my being. I had felt that the earth I walked on was less of an incumbrance. There were times when I seemed to float upon it. This feeling was both what remained of a great experience and also the beginnings of vanity. I myself had been born a son of the Gods. When I had lain with Thekla I had been attended by a Goddess. It was odd that I had never considered the possibility of issue from my nights with Thekla. It never crossed my mind once that I might beget a child, himself born of a Goddess.

It was on a day of late Spring with the rock roses alive and singing

130

in the foothills following a night of rain that Thekla said she was with child. 'It is yours,' she said proudly. It had never occurred to me that there could be any issue from her single experience with my father. I told her to gather up her few possessions. She did as I bade her, wondering and troubled. I think her feelings for the hut in which she was born were those of an animal for its lair. I took her by the hand and led her across the sunburnt wasteland between her mother's hut and the house. My father rose from the porch in which he was sitting and gave me a single look of horror and unusual comprehension. 'What are you doing?'

'She will live in the house while she has her baby.'

'You blaspheme the Gods, you have come back empty handed from Eleusis, you take this creature and rob your father of his rights, now you bring her, bring her——'

He went on saying 'Bring her, bring her,' in a broken, reedy melody, swaying backwards and forwards on his feet until he fell headlong on his face. Thekla's mother came out with a reverential roar in which there was no heart or pity but only a sense of ritual and the requirements of discipline. She helped me roll him on his back and he lay staring at the sky with one side of his face blank, expressionless and seemingly without muscle and the hand and leg on the other side totally inert. There was a dribble of saliva from the lower angle of his mouth which was lop-sided.

I told the wailing mass at my side to go for Personides though I did not need him to tell me my father had had apoplexy. Personides gave him a quite cursory examination. 'He will survive a little time.' When Personides returned next day my father had regained consciousness. There was no flicker of recognition in his engorged eye but sight seemed less important to him than word and gesture. He struggled to move his lips but no words came. I knew that he tried to move his right hand because he glanced so often towards it and the living side of his face expressed such agony at his inability to do so. Twisting his trunk, with the living half of his face contorted, he used his free arm to point constantly and slowly away from the island and in the direction of Crete. 'He is thinking of your mother,' said Personides. 'She came from Crete.'

'What do you know of my mother?'

'Nothing, except that she came from Crete and that she was too good for your father.'

'Did you know her?' I said.

'I saw her once or twice. She went from us quickly.'

'How can you say such things of my father when he is lying like this before you?'

'I could have said the same things any time in his life,' he said coolly. He prescribed some concoction of herbs to keep my father peaceful. He did not seem at all interested in his fate.

I left my father in charge of Thekla's mother and the other women slaves and went across the island to see Electra. I told her that my father had had apoplexy and would probably die. Her face was suddenly contorted with a pity which was completely sincere. Then it relaxed into a kind of glowing compassion in which she celebrated the opportunity to be more than ever a mother to me. Then I told her that I was having a child by Thekla. The colour poured downwards from her cheeks, beginning with the temples and ending below her chin. It was as though she bled from some invisible wound. She gave a frank and uninhibited shriek. In her broken accents I detected words like 'animal', and 'like the rest'.

I was so shaken by her coarse shriek, at her worst she sounded no better than Thekla's mother, that I tried to console her by hinting that our connection had on one night been sanctified by a Goddess. I had some dim hope that she would regard this as further evidence that I was promising material for development and clearly capable of a higher life. She shrieked again and ran away from me down the steep path from the headland and towards the port. As she went I saw her arms stretched rigidly at her sides with only her hands twitching convulsively but with her fingers held stiffly. It was hideous to see her like the caricature of a woman and yet to know that she suffered acutely. I heard some days later that she had taken ship to Crete. She had given out that it was in order to study in the libraries there. It seemed reasonable that this was the kind of anodyne Electra would choose. Her frigidly distinguished mother told the same tale around the port for weeks. I did not know it would be so long before I saw Electra again.

The cloudless Summer went endlessly on. I had a sense that for me things were coming to a climax which I could not define. Thekla continued to live in the house. She was gentle and loving to my father who regarded her from his sick couch with his wandering and inconclusive vision and with a wan expression of hate. Thekla's

132

mother by this time had abandoned all respect for my father. In her bull-brained thoughts he was no longer significant. She showed no respect to a breathing wreck. I kept her out of the house as much as possible. This did not affect her attitude to me which was hideously respectful and gracelessly polite. On one occasion when Thekla was weakened by being faint and sick in the morning for successive days, Nikita offered herself to me for consolation with such repulsive vigour that I pushed her out of the door and forbade her access for a number of days.

One day at the height of Summer the smell of broom was everywhere. The hill by the house was smothered with blossom and heaved before me in a golden wave. I smiled bitterly to think how idle it was to recall Daria with the whole island submerged in the smell of the blossom I associated with her. I went one morning on the hill with no more aim than a sight of the sea. I sat on one of the flat stones I had shared with Daria. Out of a void, the crystalline air, tautened and humming with the sound of the sea, I heard her laugh softly. When I turned round she was standing above me. I moved my arms across her knees because I thought she was a vision and expected them to pass through her. I felt her knees slacken as my arms went round them. 'Am I forgiven?' she said.

I stared at her, drained of every sensation but the faculty of seeing. She was there with her long fair hair and her deep-sea eyes and, above all, with her arms widening towards me and her breasts lifting under her tunic. Since we went to Eleusis she had covered her breasts. I knew that at this moment, with my mind bereft and my heart so full that it had only one feeling, the words I used could only be few. 'Is it true you love me?' I said.

'With heart, mind and body and with everything in me. With my soul, too, and with whatever accompanies us through all our lives and through the grey and green pastures of Hades and Heaven.'

'One thing I must know and I live and die by your answer. Will you leave me again?'

'Never. Not here, not in Hades, not in any other life.'

'Will you marry me?'

'Yes, when Thekla has had her baby.'

'Why wait?' I said.

'I would not hurt anyone who has given you pleasure. Do you know why I went away?'

'No. I thought sometimes it was to find something more about what we learnt at Eleusis. There are many scholars and philosophers in Crete.'

Daria laughed gently. 'You must take me for Electra. I went away because of her.'

The thin sad shadow of bitterness descended in my brain. 'You left me when you knew I adored you.'

'I left you because Electra loved you and because, deep in your heart, you loved her, not simply and naturally, but because there is a deep link between you and because you know she wants to help you.'

'And is impotent to do so.'

'That adds a little to your love of her.' Daria smiled and wound her long golden hair round my head. It was odd to feel something lighter than ripe corn streaking through the shadows of my wiry, dark hair. 'It does not alter who you love or in what way because I, Daria, have come to claim you. I set off at once when I heard Electra shriek.'

'Heard?'

'Heard with my inner ear.'

'You were with me that first night I lay with Thekla.' She looked away. 'I don't think you know it,' I continued. 'Thekla was taken over by you and you by the Goddess.'

'Nevertheless I know it. It is something very solemn. Thekla's child will be born of a Goddess.'

'That is what my father said of me. Is it true?' I said.

'It is like a lot of what your father said. It had the beginnings of truth. Now let us go to your house and see him.'

It was not a case of her seeing my father but of him seeing her. His gaze became fixed. He kept his eyes on her face. Then he smiled for the first time since his apoplexy. His smile was broken by the slanting rim of his mouth, nevertheless it was clear that he was happy to see her and she knelt beside him and held his hand. From that day onwards his nights were peaceful. He gained no strength but lay by day, with eyes closed and his eyelids only opened when he heard her coming.

After two days Daria came to live in my father's house. She maintained her home on the East side of the island and brought no slaves with her.

When Daria first came Thekla withdrew into herself like a sick animal, making no complaint, still doing her duty, still kissing my hand when she saw me but eating little food and sitting often alone. She had no bitterness towards Daria and smiled respectfully when she saw her. After two days I never saw Daria and Thekla in the evenings. Daria took Thekla to her room and they spent hours together in silence. When I asked Daria what they did together she said nothing. Thekla told me that Daria put one hand on her forehead and another on her neck and that, after that, she held her in her arms and everything seemed to dissolve and Thekla was not aware that she was separate from Daria. They seemed to become one person. After three days Thekla followed Daria wherever she went. She found excuses to repair an untorn tunic. She wove for Daria's forehead a wreath of myrtle. Sometimes they walked to the forest together. I noticed that Daria held Thekla's hand in a peculiar way seeming to caress the base of her thumb. I had never seen mistress and slave walking in this way and it perturbed me a little. I suppose I inherited something of my father's pusillanimous sense of authority.

My father faded slowly from life. He weakened in the heat of Summer and still more with the waning of the world in Autumn. As he weakened Thekla flowered. When I looked at her body she reminded me of ripe corn urgent with grain. Then one night in September, with the stars whirling visibly through the mist with the sea wind, Daria called me to my father's room. She told me to move all the slaves away. She crouched by my father's couch and held his hand. Then her eyes went blank, her cheeks duskily red and the tissues of her face seemed to swell and stiffen. Her lips sagged sideways, she drooled obscenely and I heard my father speaking thickly in blurred phrases through her. When I looked at the side of his mouth it was completely unmoving. She had taken his psyche into hers. 'Your mother is not dead. You will not find her by looking for her. I wronged her. If ever you see her ask her to forgive me.'

Daria slid to the floor. After a few moments she gazed at me with vacillating eyes and muttered indistinctly that she was well and that there was nothing the matter with her. I told her what my father had said. She understood nothing. I sat with her for hours until her eyes were shining again. She said she remembered nothing except that she had been taken over by my father. She said that it was not as with the Goddess Artemis. She had no idea what my father meant. I believed her implicitly. I did not know that the messengers of the

135

Goddesses sometimes prevaricate temporarily but only because of their compassion for us.

My father died during the night. Daria held his head and his hand always. As his breathing diminished she passed one hand to me. I could feel a fine current of coldness enveloping our bodies but a little outside them. My father passed with a smile. Daria kissed him as his breathing ceased. It was only days afterwards that I recollected how beautifully he had smiled and how, until that moment, he had had no control over the muscles of his face since the day he was stricken. It was clear that in my father's last smile his psyche had been wholly usurped by Daria.

Thekla's child was born next day. He came into the world as my father went out of it. He had fair hair at the top of his skull and deep-sea eyes like the warm, Autumnal eyes of Thekla with their animal kindless and unflagging warmth. Thekla suckled the child but Daria was constantly with him, though never in Thekla's absence. I noticed that she often laid her hands on Thekla's forehead and on the nape of her neck.

After my father died I spoke sometimes to Daria of my mother. How could we find her? Daria asked me if I had a longing to see her. I said I had no great longing but that I felt that not to do so was a kind of betrayal. She said, 'Can we wander through the whole of Crete asking every woman we see if she is your mother? Remember,' she added, 'you will see Electra. She will be only too glad to say yes.' After that we spoke surprisingly little of my mother. It was some time before I learnt that some who are the messengers of the Gods can exclude from one's mind thoughts which, from the point of view of reason, would seem to be inevitable.

Daria and I were married in the height of Summer. She was dressed in white and gold. The filet round her forehead was golden too. It was hard to distinguish it from her hair. From the centre of her forehead she wore a small crystal shaped like a diamond. It was her modest tribute to the Goddess Artemis who had watched over both of us. She carried a small sheath of unripe corn. There was a woman priestess and a priest presiding at our wedding. Both wore white robes with golden cords at their waists. The priestess handed another sheaf of corn to Daria. After she had done so she touched her forehead, then between and a little below her breasts and then low down on her abdomen. The priest lit a torch and the temple of

136

the port was blue with fumes and smelt of herbs raked at noon by the rays of the pitiless sun.

Going out of the temple I thought of Electra. I thought wherever she was it must have been a bad day for her. When we walked down the steps outside the temple I saw her watching us. She was slimmer than ever, her face was thinner and her muscles seemed harder. She never smiled. She raised her right hand stiffly, reluctantly, at right-angles to her body, by way of greeting. She could not bring herself to wave us welcome. Daria went up to her and kissed her. She did not respond. She looked at me over Daria's shoulder with, in her eyes, all the dumb accusation of which she was capable and, deeper than in her eyes, all the hopelessness and emptiness she felt when she saw me. When she withdrew from Daria's embrace I went towards her quickly. 'Come back, Electra, I say come back.'

'To whom, to what? I am going back to Crete.' She moved away from the people around us. Once again she went out of my life.

When Daria and I were alone I said, 'I feel that Electra was putting a curse on us.'

'That is the most unworthy thing you have ever said or are ever likely to say. Would a woman be happy to see the man she loved taken from her?'

'She hates you,' I said.

'I believe I love her,' Daria said slowly.

'How can you do that?'

'Because she loves you. It is all very simple.'

Waiting for the night after the wedding was to live an epoch. The air was tight and humming with the vibration of invisible chords. In our days in Greece, to and from Eleusis, we had lain together without passion or pain but now I had tasted the flesh with Thekla, with whom it had begun in desire and ended in experiences which were of other worlds. My child by Thekla was born of a Goddess. What would be expected of my union with Daria? It was this which ruined the love between us but I cannot see how the pain we suffered could have been avoided. I had drawn to me a Goddess through my lust for a slave. It was only natural that I should expect to walk between the stars in lying with someone with Daria's gifts. Had I taken her naturally, lovingly, perhaps even ferociously, all would have been well, but as she lay at my side, with our lips interlocked, as she rolled below me, moaning slightly and with her breast heaving, very much of this world in this ultimate cry of her flesh, there traversed my brain a thought like a nagging ant, 'This is where we leave this earth for the higher air where the Goddesses are drifting.'

No one could have been loved with such natural passion as Daria gave to me that night. I was more aware of her passion than I had been of Thekla's. Thekla had been lost to me in my desire for an unpretentious slave. Now, all the time I made love to one favoured of the Goddesses and acting as their messenger, I was thinking, 'She, the messenger of Artemis, is lying in my arms. These thighs curled about me belong to one to whom the Mother Goddess has spoken.' When dawn came and I could see the light extinguished in Daria's eyes I knew that no man could have been loved more totally and that no one with so much to be thankful for could have had such doubts.

It was difficult to know what Daria felt. In almost every circumstance of life her eyes were luminous with a smile always trembling on her welcoming mouth.

As the months went by I was surprised and troubled that Daria was not with child and also because I had never had with her the illuminating experience which had been mine with Thekla. Were the two things connected? Had I not been sufficiently inspired to make her fertile? At the back of my mind there was always the reverberating hammer which kept repeating, 'With Daria as your wife you should produce a child with the inspiration of the Goddesses in his brain and heart.' I felt that my failure to do so was not fate, not circumstance, but either a flaw in my character or an act of omission. I even went to see Personides. 'You yourself said I was a son of a God.'

'By your gifts, not in the way you were conceived. Every man who can see the future and the past is in a way a son of the Gods. In some ways you remind me of your father. This nonsense about producing a son of the Gods addled what brain he ever had.'

'I've more evidence than I ever told you.' I told him what had happened the second time I loved Thekla. I do not know why I spoke to him freely because he was always very brusque and seemed at times even inimical. I suppose it was because he was honest enough not to care whether I listened to him or not.

'That is something different,' he said. 'It is an experience and you have had it but this is not to say your son by Thekla will be a son of the Gods.'

'I never contemplated it.'

'Why not? After all Daria was regarded at Eleusis as a possible initiate.'

'Does that count for anything?'

'Not of itself. If the Gods decide to use you or her they will. What men wish for is always evil. What comes without effort is mostly good.' His eyes narrowed and his thin-lipped sardonic mouth tightened. 'When I speak to you I always end with a warning. This thought of children sired or mothered by divinities will be your ruin. Look, Electra infuriated you. She was always wanting you to train for something.'

'What has that to do with what I have asked you?'

'Simply that you are getting ready to train yourself for something.'

'Even if what you said was true, how could I turn off these thoughts which keep revolving in my brain?'

'That,' he said, 'is a sensible question.' He paused before answering and when he spoke again he spoke more slowly and was less irascible. 'I suppose somebody else will have to do something to help you.'

Two months later Daria told me that she was pregnant. I was overjoyed and told her of my visit to Personides and how I believed he had worked this for us. She said that this was nonsense. Personides was a man without any psychic gifts other than that of piercing intelligence. Intelligence as distinct from impressive thinking was a rare attribute and to be ascribed to the psyche. I did not pay the visit to Personides I felt I should. I glowed in the happiness reflected to me by Daria because she rejoiced so much in my own joy.

14

DARIA and I were unbrokenly happy until the last months of her pregnancy. She had been sick in the mornings in the first months but between the third and the sixth this had lessened and though her body was heavier she moved as freely as ever and we had never been happier walking the island in the Summer of that second year after our marriage. It was with the Autumn that her body seemed unnaturally swollen and distended with fluid. The sickness spread from the morning through the day. There were days in which the light went from her eyes and she dragged herself round like any sick woman. She even consented to see Personides. He excluded me from the interview and when I objected said I knew nothing about medicine and if I knew better I could get someone else. As there was no other healer on the island this was small consolation. When he had examined her he said that there was a serious poisoning of the tissues, that perhaps Daria should never have had a child. This seemed to be monstrous but he disregarded my protests and told me that in some women who do not wish for children there is a negation by the tissues of the coming child and that the organs of the body are poisoned by it.

'This is rubbish,' I said. 'Daria is so loving she would inevitably want children.'

'She wanted to please you, you fool. There are times when you remind me of your father. I think that sometimes your intelligence and the few gifts you seem to have, disguise the fact that deep in your heart and mind you are as stupid and unseeing as he was. And of course with the same preposterous ambitions. There are two kinds of women who reject children. There are those who do so because they are naturally arid and selfish. There are others who do so because they are made for a higher destiny than the continuance of life on this earth. They are too gentle to resist with their hearts and brains the desires of their husbands or their own impulses to motherhood. They resist in their tissues and the latter are poisoned. I will see her every day.'

Some days she was a little better for his visits but on other days the sickness intensified and her face was grey and drawn. She had lost her beauty. For all her agility the contours had been soft and her muscles delicate. Now she was swollen and inert. As she drew nearer to term her hair darkened. One day I thought, 'This is Electra within her,' and said so to Personides.

'You are regaining your intelligence.' This was all he said and after he had said it he changed the conversation quickly. 'The oracle has come back to the island.'

'I thought she had been drowned.'

'You yourself said you had seen a woman entering the cave. She may have inspected it and found it suitable. Anyway she has returned. You should go to see her.'

'Why?'

He grinned diabolically. 'Because you are dissatisfied with me. After all, you need someone.'

'I have Daria. Are you trying to tell me Daria will die?'

'I am telling you she will not die but will suffer greatly in order to live.'

I never dreamt to ask him about the child.

The day after this conversation when I went in to Daria she cried aloud suddenly in a dry, inhuman and high-pitched shriek. Her eyes were fixed, her limbs stiffened and then relaxed in a coarse, rippling convulsion I had seen with Antonides. I cried aloud in my agony and laid my hands upon her. It was an instinctive gesture but after I had made it I felt she had recovered, that the tumult would cease. Her body continued to writhe under my hands. What was there in me that would cure Antonides and not Daria? I called on Thekla who lay beside her on the couch with her arms around her. Gradually the convulsions ceased. I saw that Thekla had done for her with her simple and instinctive compassion what I had failed to do with my willed intention. I ran up the hill to Personides. He came down to see Daria. She was quiet then. 'I warn you,' he said. 'There will be other attacks.'

'Why could I stop the convulsions of Antonides and not those of Daria?'

This time he was sorry. 'My poor man, can't you see that you had no attachment to Antonides. He repelled you as a man but your psyche went out to him because of his sufferings. Your touch transmitted the pity of your psyche. When you touch Daria you transmit to her all the agony your human self feels for her and all your fear of losing her. There are,' he added wearily, 'so many things to learn. Go tomorrow and see the oracle.' I felt it was his way of saying that he himself could do no more for me.

When I went in to Daria that evening she was bloated and pale and her beauty was only in her eyes and smile. 'Go and see the oracle tomorrow,' she said.

'Do you say it from yourself or from Personides?'

141

'From myself, my darling.'

Next day I went up the long slope to the overhanging lip of cliff from which the goat path drops to the near shore of the narrow inlet. I went down the path and along the shore to where the inlet ended in the form of an arrow. Then I walked round the path, thinly scratched on the far side, a narrow ledge below the steep plunging rocks, and came to the mouth of the cave. I went inside the cave as far as the light from outside infiltrated. Then I heard a voice, booming and accentless, echoing loudly in my ear drums and seeming to be speaking a hand's-breadth from me. Then I saw in the wall of the rock a hole shaped like a tunnel with the thin end inwards and I knew that the oracle lived farther in the interior of the rock and that her voice was amplified by the long tunnel at its widest circumference at the level of my head. 'First of all she will live,' the voice said.

'You swear this is true?'

'I swear it.'

'Why should I believe you?'

'Why should you,' the voice said, 'but you do. Admit that you believe me.'

'I do,' I said. 'Are you man or woman? To me your voice is just a voice. It's like the rocks speaking.'

'*You* know. Now say it.'

'You are a woman. Where do you come from?'

'Where do you?' she asked.

'From the island.'

'And before that?'

'You talk in riddles.'

'It is you who make the riddles. I speak the truth. Like you I come from this earth and before it from this earth and in between my visits I live with the psyches in the other kingdoms.'

'And the child?' I asked.

'You have already a child, an unusual child, a child of the Gods.'

'And Daria's child?'

'We must wait,' she said.

'You give no hope.'

'I give no opinion. One cannot alter the pattern of destiny. We can smooth out the cracks which disfigure the pattern.'

142

'I want this child.'

'Yes.'

'But of course most of all I want Daria.'

'She wants you,' she said. 'That is why you have come to see me.'

'I came to see you for help with Daria.'

'You need help yourself.'

'Help, for what?' I said.

'You will see in time.'

I cried out so loudly that my voice reverberated more than her own level, inhuman notes from the hollow of the rocks. 'You are warning me to be ready for an unbearable loss. I want no help for myself because I cannot live without Daria.'

'I have reassured you already. She will come to no harm. Go back to Daria. If she has no more convulsions for two days come back to me here. If she has any recurrence do not return and put no trust in me.'

'I will stay now,' I said. 'I trust you implicitly.'

'No, go now. You are one of those who need a sign.'

For two days Daria rested peacefully and had no further convulsions. The third day I returned to the oracle. I came to where the light ended and where the tunnel through which she spoke began. I thought I would venture farther but her voice boomed sharply. 'Do not pass this point. Though you will hear me you must never see me. This is the only condition I make. Sit down on the ledge the other side of the cave where the darkness begins. What do you see?'

'The darkness inside and the light outside.'

'Look into the darkness. What do you see?'

'Nothing.'

'And now?'

'Something like a world. Like a world seen by a bird from high in the sky.'

'How far does it stretch?'

I told her what I saw. I saw it in the same way as I had seen the Mysteries conducted while I sat on the log with the priest and Daria and looked at the framework of pale earth and pine trees. There were lakes with, thrown across their waters, the shadows of mountains intensely dark. The mountains were covered with snow. That was the country to the North. There was also desert, flat for the most part but with heaving dunes. Then there were patches of verdure, a

143

dark burnished green sprinkled round the wells. This was the country to the South. Then there was an endless land of pale hills with the dark still smoke of rosemary and thyme in pockets on their surface. In this country there were olive groves with twisted green trees of immense age and young green vines, very light and translucent against the unlit green of the leaves of the olive. This was the Eastern area of the world I saw. Away to the West was a richer, greener immensity of forests where the trees shed their leaves in Autumn, and between the forests the corn and rye. 'What is this empire I see,' I said. 'It stretches far, far beyond Greece and for a thousand miles.'

'Look again,' she said.

Now all I saw was the country to the West. There was first a dark, quilted pattern of green forest dissected by strips of corn. It was as I had seen it in my first vision. Then, in a flash, there was no green but a blue land-locked sea, sunswept and tideless, and beyond it, through a narrow strait, an endless tormented and ugly sea. 'What do you see?' the oracle asked.

'The land is changed. The land to the West is ravaged by water. The cornland is flooded and the trees torn away by a great flood.'

'What could that be?'

'How can I say? There is one answer only but how could I have seen it? Was it the sinking of Atlantis? They all know on the island how once the land had stretched unbroken and beyond the Western sea and how, after a great earthquake, a tidal wave had engulfed the land and carved a great sea out of what was once the earth.'

'What else do you know of Atlantis?' she said.

'No more than I have been taught. They were a race of half Gods who lived away in the West. They left their world in what is now the ocean. They moved East and a little North and South but mostly Eastwards. They came to Crete and Greece and the surrounding countries. They went beyond the channel to the countries to the South. They went also to Egypt.'

'What were they like?' she said.

'Like the Gods. Like the statues of our Gods. I have heard it said that the old sculptors carved models of men from what they remembered of the Atlanteans.'

'Were these model men like us?'

'I think so,' I said. 'There were minor differences. The men's

144

breasts were fuller like the breasts of women. Their hips were a little more rounded.'

'Look into the darkness again,' she said. 'It is only by seeing through and beyond darkness that we see the light.'

What I saw, peering farther into the darkness of the cave, were two beings walking hand in hand. They were delicately made and their faces had a beauty which was untranslatable in terms of sex. Their features were small and delicate and their faces longish but not oval with unaggressive chins precisely chiselled. Their eyes were firm and soft. Their foreheads were wide and a little low and their dark hair, to the length of their shoulders, was more silky than the darkness of Electra's. They were smiling slightly. Their eyes were an intense and incandescent blue, a little like the gentians on the hills. The whites of their eyes were half luminous and in their gaze there was something hypnotic but at the same time welcoming. Under their white tunics their breasts lifted slightly.

'Are these men or women?' the oracle said.

'Men surely,' I said. 'They have the faces of remarkably refined men. They do not walk like women.'

As I watched them approach one opened his tunic. I saw breasts with small half-budded nipples like those of a girl of ten. Then the other did likewise and I saw the same delicate and unprovoking signs and symbols of womanhood. 'The Atlanteans were neither men nor women,' she said. 'They were hermaphrodite.'

'The children of Hermes and Aphrodite.'

'As you say,' she said. 'They did not multiply with their bodies.'

'But on earth that is inevitable.'

'Watch,' she said.

The figures stopped walking towards me. I saw each naked. Their thighs were delicate but not smooth like a woman's and as agile and quick moving as a man's. In this way they resembled Electra. Between their thighs was a flattened triangle with no signs of womanhood or virility. As I watched I saw a silver grey rim surrounding the contours of their bodies. This thin rim moved two fingers' breadths outwards leaving a gap between itself and the surface of their bodies. Then, between the solar plexus and the anonymous triangle low in their abdomen, a silver sac was extruded with the shape of a broad and blunted elipse. The sac itself had a silvery iridescence. Inside was a milky opalescence and within the opalescence the miniature of a living being which grew until there was nothing before my eyes but the remnants of the burst sac drifting away like mist in the shadows and before me the figure of another being.

My head felt light and when I moved I felt I would fall. 'Do not worry,' said the oracle. 'What you feel is only an echo of your malady. It will not return. What was it you saw?'

'The mode of birth in Atlantis.'

'While they stayed in Atlantis,' she said.

'Can these people be put above the Gods? When the Gods and Goddesses manifest themselves in love they use human beings in the ordinary mechanisms of love. We know that the Gods were once men and returned to earth but I cannot think these people were above the Gods.'

'The Atlanteans were not Gods. They were a higher creation than our own but essentially human. Our Gods are to some degree fabricated from our memories of Atlantis. Listen, my child.'

It was the first time she called me my child and it took me back to Ekko and Eleusis. I wondered if I would ever see her again.

'No,' said the oracle. 'You will never see her.'

'You read my thoughts.'

'No. When we are seeing together so far into the past you and I are one.'

It seemed odd that I could be at one with a being known only to me by a voice transmitted by a long cavity cut through a rock. It was odd that I never at this time wondered if the voice in the cave was Ekko's. There are those with the capacity to block as well as to stimulate the thoughts of others. I did not know that all I was now seeing and hearing was conditioning my life into an intricate, minute and logical pattern. 'How did the Atlanteans descend to our level?' I said.

'As always, by ambition. Those who wish to rise inevitably fall. It is a lesson to be learnt by worlds and individuals. You yourself will learn it. They invaded our world to the East of their own. This is one aspect, or rather an re-enactment, of the Fall of Man. It is said by some in other countries that there was once a near God or angel seized or seduced by a fallen angel. Many of these stories and suggestions are memories of Atlantis. Remember always, there is no truth but memory. The Atlanteans came Eastward and conquered

146

our world in a day. This was their fall. There are those who say that their ultimate fall was to reproduce themselves like men and women, growing in the course of time the necessary organs because at first they retained in our world the capacity to regulate their own reproduction. But this was only a secondary fall inevitable after the first. What was the true fall was the use of power for gain. It is always a demon who stimulates us to seek power over others.'

'How could they conquer a world so quickly, some legends say in a day? How could they travel so fast from Crete to Greece and across the water to the lands to the South* and up to the high snow mountains?'†

'You saw how they produced children by the extrusion of an etheric substance. The latter was not a substance as we know it. It was the flowing together of a kind of psychic life. They could reproduce in their thoughts and feelings. They could live also in the same way. When the urge to conquer came upon them – Demeter alone knows why they were so afflicted because they had everything including the impulse to move invisibly – they conquered by thoughts of dominion projected into the ether. Look again,' she said.

I saw men and women like ourselves working and walking in the fields and forests. I saw a cloud, a fine silver cloud, it seemed without menace, pass over the sun at noon. I saw all those who worked and walked stop suddenly and stand motionless. I saw the cloud descend and as it did so their eyes glazed and smiled like a woman who knows with her last pain that her child is born. Then I saw separating from the silver cloud what seemed like puffs of silvered mist. These circles surrounded the people who stood in the fields. The circling clouds cohered into elliptical forms in light, pulsating silver. Then they appeared as the Atlanteans, who in their movements seemed like delicately fashioned men and who in their gentleness were essentially women. The men and the women of our world were stunned slaves. The Atlanteans spoke to them and commanded them with their thoughts. Our ancestors responded with what they believed were their own thoughts but were unaware that their minds were in bondage. The Atlanteans brought with them an immense charge of telepathy in their etheric substance. They conquered a rich world without terror or brutality.

* Asia Minor and the Middle East.
† As far North in the Balkans as Northern Yugoslavia.

'Was this good?' said the oracle. She was always picking up the last of my thoughts when she asked me these questions.

'It gives us a hint of divinity. No, it injected into us the spark of divinity. And also it was done without bloodshed.'

'You are deluded by the harvest of benefits,' she said. 'You do not see the essential tragedy. What was the sin of Atlantis? In their own country they were able to communicate without words and without effort in the interests of love and peace. When they injected their capacity into this world they reinforced it by the power of will. It was part of an imperial intention. There is nothing more evil in the world than the exercise of will. It kills men and empires. Worse still, it drugs the psyche. You know that it is possible for the psyche itself, if not to die, to drag in coma through aeons?'

'What I do not understand——'

'Go back to your wife.' Her voice was sharper. 'Always you are preoccupied with what you do not understand. Look, you have seen. It has been given you to see. Would you rather rely on your five clear senses and the others that are hidden? Would you rather feel, see and know or would you rather think? Would you rather be yourself or Electra?'

'How do you know Electra?'

'I know many people. It is part of my trade.' I thought I detected a spectral derision in her voice but it was too amplified by the tunnel in the rocks for me to know its variations. 'Go back to your wife before you understand too much.' She paused and added, 'And notice the country on the way back home.'

'Why especially?' I said. 'I have seen it often and you know I love it. Or if you don't what you say means nothing.'

This time she laughed harshly. 'You are right to hit back. But notice the country when you go back home. Come again tomorrow.'

'How do you know I will be free to come?'

'You are not free.' This time her voice was frankly derisive but at the same time friendly. 'You will never be free. You will always be the slave of your own curiosity.'

When I left her in the cave there was no change except the electrifying transition from darkness to light. Looking into the cave the darkness was absolute. Going out the light was piercing. The air was throbbing in sheets of crystal slanted downwards from the cloudless sky. Mounting the goat path the side of the inlet under the

148

lee of the overhanging hill I noticed a change in the atmosphere. The rocks seemed to crackle. It was as though they hissed with the swish of invisible lightning. The earth in the hinterland seemed faintly humming. I felt the grass was seething with a million insects. There was no cloud in the sky. There was nothing but the earth breathing restlessly in sleep and a tremor that I felt in the tingling of the soles of my feet.

When I got home Personides was by Daria's couch. She was pale and smiling but humanly frightened. I learnt that one of the horrors of childbirth is that while it lasts those so endowed no longer live in the psyche. Her body had extracted a cruel revenge for the delight it had given.

Personides took me aside. 'The labour has started. It will be slow and painful.'

'Why?'

'Because she was not ordained for this sort of thing.'

'You mean it is my fault.'

'It is not a question of faults,' he said testily. 'You were born a man.'

'Never again will I get her with child.'

'That is wise,' he muttered. 'It is all too wise.'

In the illimitable night I heard her cry softly. When I went in to her I could see by the light of the rushes that she was weeping very little. She had bitten her lips and they were swollen and bleeding. 'Are you all right, my love?' she whispered faintly.

'I? It is you I am concerned with.'

'The pain is nothing. What is worse is the wish to give you something you want. But I want so hard to get it over and it takes so long.'

It came to me that she had not wanted the child except as the fulfilment of my own needs. She had made the radical error of living her life through another. When she transfigured me most was when she did freely, without will, whatever a bud does when it opens in the sun.

Next day there was a lull in the pains. I asked Personides if I should go to the oracle. 'Go, go, of course. It will take hours yet.' I knew that he was glad to be rid of me.

Going back along the headland I had the rare feeling of the earth being unnaturally alive and the soles of my feet were hot and tingling. It came to my mind that there was a spreading fire in the bowels of the earth but this feeling was only an instantaneous stab and all I could think of was Daria lying pale and deliberately inert, trying hard to convince me that she had no pain. But when I reached the cave and spoke to the oracle my thoughts of Daria were suspended because the oracle turned all my thoughts towards the past. My psyche was fused with hers and I saw the world through an inner eye which I shared with her but which was veiled when I left her and turned back to the world. 'Did you feel the life in the earth?' she said.

'Yes.'

'What does it signify?'

'That when I am with you I feel things more keenly. The earth is living like ourselves. Each plant, each insect has a kind of psyche. After I leave you I feel my identity with all things living.'

'That is true,' she said slowly. 'Yes, already,' she added, 'you feel the impact of truth.' It was almost as if she had been impressed by what I had said. 'Do you feel anything more?'

'Not directly. If I thought about it I could tell you more but you have warned me against the perils of thinking.'

I had learned now to distinguish her low-pitched laughter when she spoke to me through the tunnel in the wall. 'Let's go back to the past,' she said. 'We are safer with the past. Tell me what you see.'

I cried out sharply. 'I see Daria writhing in agony. She is pale with the sweat of exhaustion on her forehead. I must go back at once.'

'That is the past. She is all right now.'

'No, no, I must return.'

'You will not be wanted. Personides wishes you absent. I tell you the pain has gone. Also Daria's whole agony is of the past. She is reliving the pain of the world's creation – of its creation and destruction if we speak the truth. You should stay here with me but I will not beseech you.'

'I will stay,' I said.

'What do you see?'

'The world I saw yesterday is wholly changed. There is no clear distinction between Atlanteans and natives. There are some who bear more clearly the stature and gait of the former. There is one especially characteristic. He has assumed a darker head since he came among us. His skull is broader. His face is a little ethereal like the Atlanteans at the beginning but his features have thickened. He is more like us. His body has the grace but has lost the delicacy of the first invaders. He is more virile. He is unmistakably but not aggressively masculine. He has an unearthly beauty but is clearly of the earth.'

'Where is he standing?'

'He is standing on a plain in a country cooled by dark forests but with the parched earth between.'

'What does he see?'

'A figure in light with corn coloured hair knotted both sides like a serpent's coils. I cannot see her features. She is outlined in silver. Now she turns to gold.'

'You are passing from what the psyche sees to what is truly a vision of the Gods. Who are you seeing?'

'Is it Demeter?'

'Yes.'

'And the dark girl with the dark hair clinging to her mother is Persephone. Her hair is dark and not corn coloured like her mother's because she is destined for the underworld. The man is Pluto. He makes no movement towards her. This I am sure of, that he makes no movement. She goes away, it seems unwillingly, from her mother with her arms lifted to Pluto. If you look into her eyes you see an agony of fear and repulsion.'

'Why does she go?' said the oracle. 'Why does she go when his hands have never touched her?'

'Because he is using what is left of his Atlantean heritage. He was rare and gifted. Most of the others have forgotten their ancestors except a circle of oracles who maintained the purity of the forms of Atlantis and its immaterial gifts and who sought to free themselves from the attraction of power and the impediments of the flesh. He drained her of will and drew her to him as the Atlanteans had done when they conquered our country. Pluto was far from belonging to the circle of oracles. He was worldly and noble and selfish and giving. He was, in a word, a man. He drew Persephone to him at a moment when the vibrations of good and evil in that place were evenly balanced. It was at the time of the equinox, when the leaves fall and the sea is troubled in Autumn. As the Atlanteans in their pure state and in their own country had the capacity to transmit to each other all the vibrations of good in the universe so, once

151

descended to our world, they acquired also the power to attract the evil vibrating in their vicinity. Sometimes it was a local and sometimes a great evil. On this day when Persephone touched Pluto all the pent-up evil in the bowels of the earth burst forth in an earthquake and a chasm opened. It was into this chasm that Pluto and Persephone were drawn. The walls of the chasm held straight because the flaw in the earth was elsewhere. Lava bubbled and seethed from the fissures in the earth. The land was inundated with a black, infertile sea. Elsewhere the sea itself poured over the country and poisoned the earth with its bitter salt. Demeter survived——'

'Goddesses always survive,' the oracle interjected. I thought there was in her voice a note of irony.

'But she was not always a Goddess,' I said. 'The great mother was once a mother on earth. She had, like you and Daria, exceptional gifts. She was remembered because there was something in her, some pent-up fountain of goodness which spread around her so that after months the earth in her area became fertile again. During that period she lived on seaweed brought in from the sea. She survived on almost nothing because she was a special being with a body seeming like ours but less materialized. In his cave dwelling Pluto survived because he called on the Atlantean resources which still lived in him. His virility and physical charm were part of the superficial matter of his being. He lived among them in his etheric substance. He cared for Persephone because in that time of crisis he had returned a little to the non-aggression and gentleness of his Atlantean substance. Persephone supported his love which was not physical because with the darkness hanging over his world and the old light wakened in him he desired her only for her tenderness and beauty. The coming back of Spring was not only renewed warmth in the sun but the people resuming movement in a desolated land. Pluto left the cavern when it was safe to do so. They called this Spring because it was a coming back to the light but in actual fact it was Spring by the moon and the lengthening of twilight. When he ventured out from the cavern with the earth stable and trembling no longer – there were many earth tremors after the first great shock – he brought Persephone with him. As they came out of the cave they found in the first fissure they saw in the earth a tiny seed of germinating wheat. It had burst prematurely because it was sheltered from the wind by a collar of fallen rocks. He and Persephone wandered until they

152

rediscovered Demeter. Pluto gave Demeter the germinating grain because he loved her for her courage and patience.'

'The legend says that Pluto discovered the secret of growing corn.'

'That is where legends go wrong,' I answered firmly. 'Pluto was a man who lived in an age when corn was corn. Demeter accepted his presents with tears and they agreed that Persephone should live with him for half of the year and return to her mother for the other half. This was because Pluto wished to recover in silence, in his half year of solitude, what he had lost of his Atlantean heritage. He did not return with Persephone to the bowels of the earth. They lived apart for six months. She went back to her mother in Spring. While she was with her mother Pluto lived in that body which Daria possesses and which comes to me with the smell of broom and when I feel her presence. Persephone had come to love him——'

'Surely it was hard,' said the oracle, 'that she should be separated for six months from the man she had come to love.'

'Only on the surface,' I said. I heard my voice, higher pitched and echoing above the deepest vowels of the cavern. 'Pluto had communicated to Persephone and to Demeter this capacity to live outside time as measured by the course of the sun and the waxing and waning of the moon. That was the end of the story of Demeter and Persephone.'

'Once you said something different.' The oracle's voice was sardonic and I knew she was testing me to make me waver from the truth of what I saw. I knew she was searching my soul for the reawakening of the old demon of reason. 'No,' I said, 'I have nothing to retract. In the beginning Demeter was unique in that she surrendered her daughter to the darkness of this man of the underworld whom we have made a God. She recognized that in this world she must either compromise between good and evil or die of an excess of either. But this compromise was not made out of cowardice but from love and pity. So that when we speak of Demeter as the God who created the world we do not insult her by regarding her as a Goddess who created both good and evil and called the evil good or justified it as good for our character simply because she had created it and wished to retain her reputation for omnipotence. But later, when she and Persephone were united for the first time and she saw the change in Pluto, all three achieved that fusion between good and evil which dispenses with the existence of either so that there were no opposites of good and bad, of beauty and ugliness, of fertility and barrenness but a unified triad. You can, if you like, call Demeter, Persephone and Pluto a Holy Trinity, the Mother Goddess, her daughter who inherited her love and pity and Pluto, the outnumbered male, as men should always be outnumbered in the divine pantheon and who carried an angel and a demon in his composition.'

She laughed again. 'You speak of Demeter and Pluto as divine but previously you had spoken contemptuously of those who worshipped them in this way. You have said repeatedly that such beings were only men and women inflated by legend.'

'And I still say it,' I cried vehemently. 'They are only Gods because they increased their powers after death and have also the capacity both to return to us and to send their messengers to us.'

Now she spoke softly. 'I see you are not to be shaken because you know the truth.'

'How long was the fall of Atlantis before the great shock that gave these opportunities to Demeter, Persephone and Pluto?'

'We do not deal in time,' she said. 'There are still those who have learnt the malformed story from their mothers. The truth is better known in Egypt where the disaster of Atlantis was graver than elsewhere. The huge tidal wave engulfed and poisoned the cornland. Millions perished from the wave and millions from the years of famine which followed after.'

'Do I need to go to Egypt?' I asked her.

She paused before she answered. 'It will not be necessary,' she said harshly. 'There is a folk memory of Atlantis. There is a memory in the common consciousness we inherit from our ancestors but only if you can read it. There is also a minority who look back clear to Atlantis and inherit its gifts and' – now her voice dragged slowly – 'as well as its gifts its dangers. There is something you must do.'

'What is it?' I said.

'You must go back to Daria and tell her the truth about life as you see it.'

'That is an immense commission.'

'I mean you must tell her what you have seen today.'

'In her present state?'

'When you return she will be living an interval without pain. You have to see her because what you have seen is true.'

Suddenly, idiotically, my heart exulted. 'And my child will see still more. He will surpass all I have seen. Because of what few gifts there are in me, most of all because of Daria, he will truly be a son of the Gods.' I spoke not entirely from vanity but because of my relief after a great strain. I was exhausted by my concern for Daria and looking into the far past was immensely wearying. I felt the life oozing from my feet and that the earth was dragging me towards it.

'Don't be a fool and commit the sin of Pluto.' Her voice was high and all of a sudden she seemed impatient and frightened. I never heard her in such a mood before. 'You go now and tell Daria the truth. Then go to Electra and tell her the same.'

'Electra? She hates me and most of all Daria. Why should I tell her?'

'She hates you a little because she loves you much. Have pity on her. You cannot condemn her for being different to you.'

'But why should she know?'

'She is one of two people who love you. Now go,' she said. 'I have other things to say later.'

When I went back scrambling up the path to the rock the sky was cloudless but in some way darker. It was as though a sheet of metal had been laid across it. This high hard glitter was reflected in the sea. The air was taut. It twanged and vibrated like tight-stretched cords. There was no wind blowing from the sea. I had noticed that the night before there had been no land breeze. The whole of the island had seemed drained of air. My temples were aching and my head was bursting. I felt as though my brains would spill and my heart thumped slowly, laboriously against my chest wall. I felt that it, too, would break.

When I got back to Daria she was suffering no pain but her cheeks were sunken. Her eyes were smiling but devoid of life. There was death in her face and I thought with horror of my imbecile exaltation early that morning when I had anticipated great powers and glory for my son to be. I saw at that moment the dark, headlong fall of a lark from the heavens to a patch of desert grass. The lark's descent represented both the collapse of my mood and the destiny of man.

I told Daria miserably, like the priest of a disused cult reading a litany to the birds and serpents, what I had said to the oracle and how the latter had described it as true. Before I mentioned her name Daria said, 'Go at once to Electra.'

It terrified me that she knew already what the oracle had advised. I knew she could read my thoughts and the thoughts of certain others and often at a distance. But now I saw her capacity to see and hear beyond human senses as a sign of her approaching death. 'I won't, I won't leave you,' I cried.

'You love me. I am sure, so sure, you will want to please me.'

So I went back over the headland not moving towards the cave but inclining to the sea port. I saw a ledge of cloud above the sea between the island and Crete. The cloud was dark with its rim towards me. I could see the sea below it and the sky above. It was an unwavering dark line traced across the ether. It was as though some maleficent God had drawn his finger across something to be obliterated. When I arrived at Electra's house I was met by her statuesque and chilling mother who said her daughter would not wish to see me. I cried out harshly, 'She should be given a chance.'

She looked at me with an indefinable expression in which terror was mixed with disdain. I have never known before that one could be afraid of what one despised. Then I heard movements in the porch behind her. I saw Electra's head, very dark in the shadows. There was perpetual night in her downcast eyes. She moved towards her mother and touched her arm gently. The smile she gave to her mother was no naturally sweet and understanding that it surprised me. As she turned to me her features folded up like a door closing. 'Come towards the harbour. Say what you must say and say it quickly.'

I told her tersely, monotonously, all I had said to the oracle and how the latter had described it as the truth. 'Why tell me?' Electra said.

'Because I felt I wanted to.'

'Liar,' she said. 'You spoke because you were told to.'

'Electra, Electra. You cannot know how I miss you.' I meant every word I said at the moment I said it. I was reliving her tenderness to me in childhood.

'This woman you married has tired you already. She has thrilled you with her lusts and now you are exhausted.'

'I think she is dying.' I spoke without resentment. It needed will and intention to extrude the words.

I dared not look at Electra. After a pause I felt her take a deep breath and exhale what she had breathed in a protracted sigh. 'I still love you but there is no happiness in love. But thank you for telling me.'

I was so moved that she still loved me that I stopped in my tracks. I did not hear her when she moved away from me. When at last I turned she was walking back home.

Later that day the pains returned. With the coming back of the pains Daria stroked my hand. It amazed me that in her agony her fingers were untensed. 'It will come this time.'

Now her lips were blue and I felt her heart was failing. I thought it would not come, not now or ever. Personides came while I sat with Daria. 'It goes on too long,' he said. 'The womb is exhausted. It cannot contract further. Either it comes or is forced or——' He looked at the ceiling.

'Or what?' I said.

'One cannot really tell,' he said helplessly. I knew he foresaw all that would happen. I knew that his mind was on me as well as on Daria and the child and that he feared for me equally. 'Why don't you go back to the oracle?' he said.

'And leave her here?'

'The pains are coming again. One had best fight them alone.'

'It stabs me to the heart but it does not repel me.'

'Nevertheless you should go,' he said.

Now, going back across the headland, it was past twilight and the sky was darkening. There was still no breath of air above land or sea and the unwavering menace of the line of cloud was exactly as it had been but intensely dark. When the stars came out they were empty of light. At first I thought this was my own mood and that the world outside me was dying and drained by my own agony. Then the moon came up chalky and lightless. It was scarcely reflected in the sea. I wondered if some catastrophe were impending. I reverted in my fear to the old hypothesis of the Gods being angry. Then it came to me that the thoughts and depressions in my own head were part of the suspended life in the air and the sea, that I and the elements depended on each other and that, worse than my acquiring the moods of the sea and the caprice of the sea wind, they, in their turn, accumulated tension from the anguish inside me that beat against my brain. Then there came to me the terrifying thought, 'You are another Pluto. You remember back to his day, just as he looked back to his life in Atlantis. In a way you are made as he.' It seemed to me in that dark moment that I had trapped Daria in my love and desire for her but there was no Demeter to be a comfort to us.

I was gripped by this thought. Were we on the brink of a great cataclysm? At that moment the sky went black and the stars went out but I knew in an instant that this was just a reflection outwards of the darkness in my heart and that I was too puny to cause a cosmic disturbance. I felt so desperate, so empty, that I called aloud to the unpitying night, 'There is no Demeter.'

The voice came back from the mouth of the cave before I had entered it and before even I had crossed the inlet. 'Go back to Daria, go back at once.'

'Is she Demeter?' I screeched. At that moment I was only concerned with my own isolation.

'Go back to her.'

'Is it she or another?' I cried to the night, shameless and terrified. 'Where is my mother, either my mother on earth or the Mother Goddess?'

'Go back to Daria.'

The oracle was not speaking with the awesome neutrality her voice assumed in the tunnel in the rock. Her voice was near my ear and had I been less frenzied I might have known it better.

When I returned home I could not at first understand why I had been recalled so suddenly. Daria lay on the couch with her eyes closed. She was certainly as still as death but I saw an imperceptible lift of her breast as she breathed faintly. Her eyelids fluttered a little as I entered the room. Personides came up softly behind me and put his hand on my shoulder. 'She will live,' he said. 'You will have her with you until the end.'

'And the child?' I said. Even then I did not know. We can see back to Atlantis and read the thoughts of others in far countries but in the midst of our own agonies and surrounded by the torture of our own lives, we see less than children.

He took me to the next room and I saw the son of the son of the Gods, the child who would be different, who would see back to the beginnings of the earth, the beginnings of life, the world's end and beyond it. His skin was blue and his limbs and body stiffened. His eyes were closed and his eyelids suffused. His face was not agonized nor his cheeks excavated. He looked merely puzzled, as though the mystery of life and of death had been too much for him. In a way he was like his father.

'There is nothing to be done,' said Personides. 'At one time it seemed we might lose his mother. She must have no other children.'

'Of course,' I said.

'She was martyred by choice. She felt the need to satisfy your love for her body and her own maternal feelings. On the other hand she was reluctant to imprison another soul in matter and to darken its wings with the evil of the world.'

'I understand,' I said. 'It is all my fault.'

'It is not your fault,' he said wearily. 'Remorse is a luxury you cannot afford at this moment and particularly when it is not merited. You must think of her.'

'Yes,' I said obediently.

'Go back to the oracle.'

'No.'

'Every man needs a mother.' He was muddled, uncontrolled and his face distorted. 'What I mean is that every man at some time needs to be as near as he can to the Mother Goddess.'

'I have Daria.'

'Go in to see her.'

I went in to see Daria who lay with her eyes closed and her eyelids inseparable from her still, cold cheeks. If she was the agent of the Mother Goddess the latter was sleeping. 'Go back to the cave,' Personides repeated. 'I will stay here with her. She will recover very quickly.'

Going back to the cave it was dark and moonless. There was no glow reflected from the stars. The wide dark cloud had intensified to a thin dark line. Under the line was a spectral opalescence. The sea was an immense grey and above its surface hovered the tarnished exhalations of evil spirits. I reflected that Spring was here and that behind me the almond trees were ghostly in the night and whispered of the coming of Summer. I could not exclude the thought from my mind that birth was death. The almonds were flowering and my son was dead. Spring was here and in every leaf bud was the death of Autumn. Daria lived the Spring in the light of her eyes, in the fullness of her smile, in the free swinging eagerness of her body. Nevertheless though she lived the Spring she carried death in her tissues. The child was lying dead and alone. He was wiser than I was. He had seen the mystery of life and had turned away from it. He had been satisfied to sense the closeness of the world and to let it pass.

Going down the goat track from the overhanging rock to the near shore of the inlet I came out of the death within my heart and saw how starless it was, how I walked by instinct and how the world had darkened. There was no light anywhere. I saw at that moment my unity with the Cosmos. The darkness in my heart obscured the world. Then the imp of reason within me told me this was nonsense, that what cast shadows in my heart was the loss of my son and the agony of Daria. Nevertheless whatever I thought, the world seemed so blank about me and the air so thickened that it seemed the darkness was something exhaled by myself and that the closing in of the world was induced by the contractions of my own heart. I stumbled along the thinly pencilled track on the far side of the inlet. I felt the mouth of the cave not by sight but by the cold stillness of the air framed within its orifice. The oracle spoke as soon as I had come level with the mouth of the channel chiselled deep in the rock. 'May the Goddess bring you peace. Your son is sleeping. He will awake and return.'

'I will not be here.'

'I cannot say. It seems we return blindly to the earth but there are instances when our hearts beat suddenly and we remember the man who walked past us as an old, old love. All that is something to be felt in another life.'

'I want no other,' I said. 'All I desire is annihilation.'

There was a pause and a kind of shrill silence in which all the Furies of the world seemed to be shrieking. 'Don't say that,' said the oracle. 'What we say and think quickly may sometimes come quickly. Try to think of Daria.'

I thought of Daria as I thought of the sun. I could not visualize her lying in the room with her sealed eyes, her face like marble and her breast moving almost imperceptibly. Thinking of Daria was no good. In my brain a cloud went over the sun and I said to the oracle, 'I feel that the suspense in the air and the darkness over the sea comes from within me, perhaps from my heart.'

'Think beyond yourself, or better still, look.'

So I looked as I had done for her before and saw Daria struggling to exclude the baby from her body. Then I saw how, with every

160

paroxysm of her pain, the world had darkened and the stars gone out. I saw that Daria's pain was a world in agony. I saw that, when she lay silent between the pains, with the sweat of exhaustion on her brow, and her skin tinged yellow by the poison in her tissues, that this was not only the forced inertia of her exhausted flesh but the breathless suspense of a world in agony, of a world that was due to die. Then I felt the darkness constricting in my heart and it seemed that what was threatened was not the country and the sea around us but the small world of our own island. I struggled upwards to the light from the darkness of my thoughts and cried aloud, 'How can this be? I have felt destruction strike through my heart. How can my nerves conduct the lightning of the Gods? Is some catastrophe awaiting us? Will it strike through me?'

'I am with you,' she said. She did not answer my question.

'Can I be an agent of destruction for what I love, the broom, the almonds and the murmuring sea. Am I worse than other men?'

'Better than most,' she answered. 'Imperfect, too human but definitely better.'

'How can a great evil be transmitted through me?'

'You cleansed Antonides of his illness. These days he is never sick. What you did was good and few others in Crete or Greece are capable of it.'

'What other evil must be cleansed through me?'

'You yourself left Eleusis because of its growing contamination with evil. You saw how the Mysteries were being tarnished. You were born in a bad age. In all your rebirths you will be born at the death of civilization and in epochs of great tyranny. Let us talk no more of these things. You are what you are and you need comfort.' She paused and added, 'My heart bleeds for you.'

'Can the heart of an oracle bleed?'

There was an endless and searing moment before she answered, 'Yes.'

In that moment I lived the whole of my life from my birth to the present. 'So you are my mother,' I cried.

'Yes.' When she answered her voice was so low, so unaffected by the resonance of the tunnel that I knew it at once as Ekko's.

'I should have known it. You are Ekko and my mother. You left Eleusis and came back to Crete and from Crete to this island to help us. Why was it I did not know?'

'We turned your mind away from the turmoil of too many questions. Daria and I blocked your mind as the Atlanteans did when they came to this country.'

'As Pluto did when Persephone came towards him?'

'Yes.'

'And the earthquake followed,' I said.

'Pluto drew towards him the beauty of Persephone and the evil of the earthquake.'

'So the island is threatened,' I said.

'You must leave the island.'

'When?' I was thinking of Daria. It did not matter to me.

'In three days' time,' said Ekko.

'She will not be fit to move.'

'She will be well in three days. People like her can absorb the whole world's sorrows in their psyches and will rise again in three days. You must tell Electra and Thekla and her mother. Personides will tell the other people on the island.'

As we spoke I could hear outside the tiny gurgle of water in the inlet. Here, far from the sea, there were no waves but only a murmur of water, at times almost inaudible when the wind was fallen. I thought of the stubborn and exquisite plants struggling for life between the fissures of the rocks. I saw the other inlet, the water lilies blanched still further by the light of the moon and the body of Artemis reflected in it. I saw the hill, a dark curve at dawn, over which Daria had come the first day I saw her. I saw Thekla sitting with her baby in the sun and the pride in her face when I sat beside her. At that moment the island seemed dearer to me than ever before. I even saw with affection my father's capers at the Spring festival. I blamed myself for not seeing his decoration of himself with vine leaves as the idiosyncrasies of a lovable child.

'You give us three days?' I said.

'The signs from the earth say four or five. Myself I would make it three for safety.'

Because life in the island was threatened everything about it was suddenly sacred and even its absurdities were something to be loved. My mind kept reverting to my father and his belief that he had sired a son of the Gods. 'Why should he believe it?' I said.

Ekko spoke very solemnly. 'Because he knew I wished to be an

162

oracle. Your father's pattern of thinking was very simple. Oracle, priestess, messenger of the Gods and ultimately Goddess. He built in his mind what he wished to see.'

'But were there no visions of a Goddess the night I was conceived?' I hated asking her these questions but I felt pressed to do so by an invisible agent. Also there was little time.

She laughed briefly but without bitterness. 'When you were conceived? Do you know the circumstances? Your father drunk, myself drugged with a potion he had mixed with my wine. In the two days I knew him he learnt that I came from Crete and that I aspired to be a priestess. That was enough for your father.'

'This is revolting.'

'Not revolting,' she said. 'You are before your time. It was a natural consequence of the way we are made. And remember that your father's reputation remains unblemished. It was the season of the Dionysian rites and your father, as you know, was most devout.' Her laughing disbelief in these orthodoxies lightened my heart for the space of a moment.

'So much for my being a son of the Gods.'

'Personides was right when he said that you, like many, were a son of the Gods as a result of your own gifts. The idea that there was a divinity attending your birth is a little coarser than irony.'

'Do you know that I believed that with Daria I could produce someone with the gifts of Apollo?' I found myself talking to her without reserve of all the imbecilities of my own fantasies. I understood now why I had spoken so freely to her at Eleusis. I had recognized then, below the level of thought, the tie of blood and of love between us.

'You could never have had such a child by Daria.'

'Why?'

'Just from wanting it too badly.'

'So much for the sons of the Gods,' I said.

'You forget there is Thekla's son.'

'Do you think——?' I said.

'Let us do no more thinking. We can only wait. Now,' she continued, 'you must go, my son.'

'Without seeing you?'

'Without seeing me.'

'Why, why?' I implored.

'I, too, ask why. Do you think because I am an oracle I have lost my feelings? We must not meet again.'

'Why?'

'Because simply to do so would be unbearable.'

'What will happen to you?' I asked.

'I will go the third day.'

'I cannot leave you,' I said. 'How can I leave you, perhaps for ever?'

Her voice changed suddenly. Once again it was booming and impersonal. 'Go now.' There was something in her voice which forced me to obey her. I left without asking how she would leave the island.

I do not know how I brought myself to leave her. In the space of an hour I had found and lost my mother. It was not merely the question of loving an earthly mother. Because she spoke to me with authority and only as a voice she was to me at least a semblance of the Mother Goddess. When I stumbled away from her along the far shore of the inlet I felt like a lost child and to me the darkness of a single night over our small island was all the mystery of the universe. But when I returned there was colour in Daria's cheeks and her eyes were opened. She moved her lips dreamily. What she said was so simple and platitudinous that I could only weep with relief that she had spoken again and been moved by a simplicity which seemed to me childlike. 'Love lasts for ever,' was all she said. I did not know that her childlike words were a truth and protection.

I said to Daria, 'Did you know that Ekko would return?'

'Yes. I saw her often and secretly when I left the island and went to Crete. I went to learn from her what was best to do for you. At Eleusis she had told me that you and I would come together but that before we did another would love you with her mind and another with her body. That was how you suffered with Electra and learnt with Thekla.'

'Why didn't she tell me she was my mother?'

'Because there was no menace. She would never have told you had there been no danger.'

'Why?'

'Because you are one of the few born free. She did not wish to bind you to her because she was your mother. And also seeing you was a great agony to her.'

164

'She hid it well,' I said.

'Half of life is hiding our reaction to pain.'

The next day I told Daria and Thekla what threatened the island. Daria was amazingly stronger. She said that Ekko had been with her that evening not in her own body but in one identical with it though without substance and through which she could pass her hand. Then a figure outlined in light and against a background of light, with serene, all-pitying eyes and wearing a filet with a diamond on her forehead, had bent over her and touched her and I knew it was Artemis who hunts and heals and who in our island was the favourite messenger of the Mother Goddess. With her renewed strength Daria said she would be able to move on the third day. Thekla looked at the dark line in the sky with the uncomprehending awe of one who knew the existence of the Gods but was unequipped to study their ways. Now at that moment the sun was obscured and its light coming over and under the line of dark cloud was hazy and sulphurous and the air immobile. Thekla wiped the sweat from our child's body. She received my attentions with her usual smile.

Seeing Electra was more difficult. From the port the sky looked darker with the shadow of the headland but I knew this thought was a passing comfort. Behind the widening, motionless and airless cloud the sun still shone but its glow was lightless. There was no light reflected from the flat, steel sea.

I did not enter Electra's house. I stood at the porch and awaited her coming. I told her what I had heard from the oracle and that Personides was warning the island. She said, 'All this is merely peasant superstition.'

'Can't you feel it in the air?'

'You mean the superstition?' she said acidly.

'I can feel it in my feet,' I said desperately.

'A son of the Gods,' she said. Suddenly she changed from sneering to a tremulous and unwilling tenderness. 'You did this for love of me.'

'It was the least I could do.'

She winced when she heard me say 'the least'. I told her I had chartered a boat to Crete and asked her to come in it with her mother and servants. She said 'No' and I left her with her face contorted and her dark eyes aching with the wish to weep.

Towards the end of the second day the earth to me was crackling with life, the black cloud had widened and the sea was lifeless. It lay unbreathing and turbid. It was as though the light from the sea had flowed into the earth. For the most part the people on the island were afraid. Some were grateful to Personides and to me for spreading the warnings, some were uncomprehending and made no comments and expressed no thanks, while others muttered that Personides had contrived this by magic and a few believed that I was his assistant. It was odd to think that people could believe that any sane man could will destruction. It was all the more horrifying to me because there persisted at the back of my mind this hideous thought, sometimes quiescent, sometimes uncoiling like a dark reptile, that there was something in me that drew down darkness and evil into my own breast and dispersed its vibrations in my vicinity.

The worst feeling was directed against the oracle. They knew somehow, by the mass malevolence which needs a scapegoat, that she had lately arrived on the island. There was no link of reason between this and the second thought which followed inevitably, that because she was new to us she must be the source of our impending misfortunes. This feeling intensified when at midnight on the second day the earth rumbled. I could hear the cries of the people in the port. I went to the headland but by the time I arrived there the night was silent and the people appeased and the clamour died down in the port below me.

We were due to leave at noon on the third day. In the morning I saw Electra, her mother and her household coming towards me. Fear had sapped Electra's pride and she was ready to leave the island. Or was it for love of me? Daria was miraculously on her feet. She widened her arms to welcome Electra but the light went out of the latter's dark eyes and while they waited they stood apart from each other. Personides was with Daria. His mood was sombre and he sat dejected with his shoulders slumped. It seemed now as though Daria was radiating her new-found strength to her exhausted physician. Or perhaps he had given more than he knew, more even than the healing vibrations of his psyche. Perhaps a little of his spirit had entered into her.

Thekla sat very patiently holding her child, smiling at the darkness of the sky and the future because, whatever the Fates, she had faith in me. I wondered at that moment if hers was the highest form of love because it never strayed beyond its immediate object and was so beautiful in its totality. She never felt or thought beyond

166

caring for the baby and pleasing me. It did not matter that I was wedded to Daria. I vow that she mourned our lost child as much as Daria. I do not think it ever occurred to her to accuse me or be hurt by my paying so little attention to her. You can say that she was a slave and pretty and it was to be anticipated that sooner or later I had my will of her and that, if it was ordered, she would bear me a child. All this had happened according to the harsh biology of our island existence but in that moment I felt that something unbelievably pure radiated from her not because of her gifts but because of her submission. She acquiesced in the dictates of destiny and there was no bitterness in her. I do not know if this was newly developed wisdom on my part or whether that morning I saw things clearer than ever before because I was divested of myself with the storm gathering about us. In my psyche I was living beforehand all that would happen when the storm would break.

Daria, Personides, Thekla and her child and Thekla's bull-like mother, bellowing her self-pity at the lowering sky, were all sitting together at the beginning of the slope which led to the overhanging rock. They waited there to be carried to the port. It was ridiculous rather than painful to see Electra and her mother separated from the others. Even in their affliction they needed to be different.

Even with the hate of the people appeased it never occurred to me to leave Ekko. The idea of taking her with us had never formed in my mind but was written in my heart and in my deeper tissues. I knew that I could never leave the island without her. Daria and Personides supported me in this. Nevertheless when I went up the slope to the overhanging rock I could feel the increased anguish behind me. The sky seemed darker than ever but I was reassured because, though the earth was tingling beneath my feet, there was no feeling of the world swinging and no crumbling revolt in the unexplored labyrinth between the open headland and the world's dark centre. Because of some tender and premonitory instinct I looked back. It is something forbidden in the crucial hours of destiny. I saw that both Daria and Electra had left the group and were moving towards me. Electra went ahead as though she had most claim on me. She had known me longer and wanted me all the more because she could not have me.

I looked beyond Electra across the island to the mountain. I saw it clearer than life with the beauty it had never shown before because

167

already I was divested of myself and seeing only with my psyche. I saw the island without the darkness of impending catastrophe. Behind, where the almonds were in flower, the folds of the country and the crevices between the rocks were sprinkled with the fitful snow of the white Spring when you saw the sky between the cloud of petals. To the North the silver of the olives was not yet quickened by the light of Summer. Seen across the almonds they were darker than green. The groves of olives marched in light and shadow to the solitary mountain. I thought of the mountain in the heat of Summer with the sky unremittingly blue behind it and sometimes above it, a glaze of cloud that looked less like vapour than congealed light.

It was no good thinking of the Summer. I walked up the last slope before the land drops to the inlet. Electra caught up with me and walked breathlessly beside me. 'Don't go to the oracle.' She was wholly pitiful in her fear and love.

'Once you wished me to consult all the oracles and priestesses in existence.'

'Not now, not ever again.'

'There is no need to worry. I will come back,' I said. My voice was a long way off. I was talking to myself as well as to her. I was not only beyond her but outside myself.

Suddenly Electra jolted back by an effort of will to a chilling exhibition of self-control and reason. 'Why are you so gentle?' she said.

'Is that a bad omen?' Neither my laughter nor my voice belonged to me now. They replaced the lost murmur of the sea.

She shivered and said nothing. She made no attempt to detain me but held her hands downwards as though she had abandoned even the impulse to supplicate. Her face shrivelled to a sharp triangle. The pupils of her eyes were drawn down like shutters. She was peering and seemed to be blind. I saw her as she would be in great age, but I knew I would not be here in this island which I would see no more with my own eyes and feel no more with my soul the heartache of its beauty. I knew I would be separated from them on another plane in which the future, like the past and the present, would dissolve in the reality of indivisible time.

I looked back to the foot of the slope where Daria was moving slowly and weakly, much more slowly than Electra, with one hand raised in farewell. She was always of the earth and even at that moment the raising of her hand was a gesture of nature, like the first sheaf of bronze on the branch of a willow or the drifting spiral of gold leaves in Autumn. The sun shone on the light gold hair and glowing blue eyes which came from her Hyperborean ancestors. The day I first saw her coming over the hill she seemed to be incarnate in light. It was like that at the end. I knew deeper than my mind and heart the meaning of the words which hummed in my brain like a lute in a sea wind, 'the end was in the beginning'.

The thought within me was itself vibrating and its truth re-echoed in my deepest tissues.

As I reached the summit of the slope I saw Daria with her hand raised and Electra with her arms lowered and empty and I saw what was the difference between them, that Daria had given so much and was still giving and that to do so was natural to her, like the gush of water from a fountain or coolness from the sea wind or peace at night. I saw that with Electra there was, as well as the urge to give, the impulse to lead, to help and in so doing to stumble into the darkness of great effort so that in the end she took from others and herself needed succour. So, standing on the summit of the slope, I waved goodbye to both and looked away, for what I did not truly know was the last time, at the almonds in flower and the tongue of the inlet where the water lilies lay on the tideless water waiting to open in the light of moonrise.

Suddenly the sky cleared and the sun came out. I was filled with hope. There would be no catastrophe. I wondered whether what I saw was real or whether it was a reflection of the changed weather in my heart. Was I seeing with my soul? Was all I had loved been crystallized for me in a final moment?

I looked across the narrow inlet to where the path wound round the rocks to the opening of the cave. In the shadow of the rocks the water in the inlet was a dark grey-blue. Beyond the point, beyond the last ragged outcrop that embraced the cave, was the light of noon. The blue of the sea was unscarred and limitless, an eternity of light and water deeper than human life because it was composed of primordial elements beyond the tarnish of suffering. I stood for a moment looking at the mouth of the cave. It was strange that, in passing to it from the world outside, there was today no gradations of light to darkness, no web of grey stretched between its walls, no film palpitating with reflections from the inlet.

Suddenly I was out of my body as never before in my life. I was not merely separated from myself but infinitely far above where I stood looking round the point to the immensity of the sea. I was a vulture hovering above myself and poised to strike. I was the instrument of my own destruction, the hand raised to pierce my own heart but far, so immeasurably far from myself that, in what I lived in those moments, there was no pain but an image of the world as it had always been with an added shadow of inevitability hanging over it. I did not suffer in that moment. I saw that what I was traversing was an illuminated hell, something projected in light against the background of the earth for the instruction of others. Certainly I lived an immensity of pain. What was unique was that I did not suffer from it. I lived the horror of those moments, the pain of the world, and most of all the horror that was coming to the island, but what I lived and suffered was contained in the infinitely small and shrinking corpuscle which zigzagged absurdly below me in the blue of space. There was certainly a pain, a ridiculous echo of personal feeling, like the overplucked note of the lute, when I thought of the dying of the island but even its death seemed in some way distant.

The arrowhead of my psyche plunged like a bird of prey and I staggered with its impact. Once again I was in my body and walking round the 'U'-shaped path which straightened in the last few paces before the entrance of the cave.

The day was still bright, there was no dark cloud, once again the fear had gone from my heart. There was no vibration of the earth beneath my feet, no subterranean growl and the earth breathed freely. I wondered if I had strayed into the past or future and if it was the present which had been hidden from my eyes.

I passed from the light of February, which was purer than any because it was the first wakening of the year and the day was moving to the climax of noon, to the darkness of the cave. Now there was no residual comfort of light in the first few paces, no feeling of the sun clinging protectively between the shoulders. There was the sensation of a curtain falling behind me, of being separated from the sun and light by a shutter of ice. For the space of a second I wondered how I would speak to my mother. Would I call her first or wait for her voice? But in the instant that followed a world ended. I was no longer outside myself. I longed for the detachment from the world I had known when I launched through the sky moving like a comet away from my own pains, from the burning eyes of Electra, hungry and unsatisfied, and from those of Daria, still luminous because she at least was satisfied and peaceable because her heart was dead within her and dead beyond waking. Now I was locked within the smallest molecule of my being. I was a still smaller atom struggling within the nucleus of the tiniest cell.

Locked up within this searing cameo of existence was all the good and evil in the world. In that moment I felt that I lacked substance and was no more than concentrated action. All the good and evil in the world were concentrated in my heart and my heart itself was no more than their point of impact. Then the evil rose in a great wave from the floor of the cave. It dripped from the roof and moved purposefully from the side walls. I knew with the piercing, irrefutable intelligence of doom that I was feeling evil as a force beyond anything I had felt before or even spoken of. Then the thought which was itself palpable like a weapon and as tangible as the force of evil, came out of the air and wound itself through the smallest interstices of my being. A voice which I recognized as my own immensely amplified was echoed back to me. 'You have drawn into this place all the evil in the world.'

When I cried, 'No, no', the voice came back, 'Not all the evil for all the world, but enough to destroy what has been your world.'

At this moment I did not know that I was held in the tentacles of the Fates and that resistance was useless. I saw, by a dim process which made my last minutes in the life beyond the cave like a far memory, the leaves of the myrtle burnished in the sunshine. I heard the humming of the first bees searching the flowers of the rosemary which seemed to have drifted on inaudible waves and clung to the darkness of the aromatic branches. I saw Daria and Electra on the hillside, now closer to each other, Daria light because of the radiation of her eyes and her soul and body which were all of the sun, and Electra dark because what came from her was written in the mystery of the moon and had been too subtle for my comprehension. I did not accept that the Fates had touched me. I was lost and afraid and called for my mother. She answered immediately. Her voice from the interior of the cave was enormously accentuated and sharpened to a screech by its agony. 'Go, go,' she cried.

'I cannot go without you.'

'Go, only go.'

'I cannot go without my mother.'

'Go, go,' she repeated. 'Love is best unspoken, even better unseen.'

I could tell by the urgency of the wail in her voice that she was as human as I was and fallible and failing. I knew in that moment that she would not fail me because of what was left of her human love for me. 'Listen carefully,' she said. 'You are looking not for me but the Mother Goddess. You saw her by the spring under the big bent fig tree, once as a boy and once with Daria. You cannot look for her in this place. Demeter did not look for Persephone in the darkness of the cave. Her daughter came back to her. You do not need the Mother Goddess. Go back to Daria. She will draw the Goddess to her perhaps twice more in a lifetime. Why go on searching? Leave that to Electra. Turn now, go back. Forget that I live and forget the Mother Goddess.'

'I want *you*, my mother.' I spoke piteously like a deserted child.

I do not know if the laughter in the cave was my own or my mother's or the Furies incarnated from the evil about us. I think it was my own laughter because my mother was not mad but only distracted and all she had built into herself as an oracle had fallen away like a disintegrating garment. 'We cannot turn back,' I said. 'We cannot stop ourselves answering questions as we can stop a wheel turning with our hands. Come back, come away, let us go to Crete.'

Then there was a pause. I waited in anguish for an answer from my mother. Then I heard her screech. 'Pluto is using you. He is of the darkness. We are of the light. You take darkness within you to save the people. But I am your mother and see it otherwise. Go, save yourself, let the people perish.'

'I will not go without you,' I said.

When I heard her speak again her voice had faded and I could not hear her words. She said, 'I am coming towards you because my spirit is broken and because you yourself will not leave without me. We do not belong to ourselves.'

I could not hear her coming towards me. Perhaps she only hovered in her psyche.

After that there was nothing in the cave but an unbreathing darkness and the conviction, almost concrete, that I was an instrument designed to draw all the evil of the world upon myself and that

172

it was concentrated on me in this moment. Now I was beyond the grip of the Furies. The fall of Orpheus had been easier. He had only suffered at the hands of possessed human entities. I felt all the darkness in the world running through my veins instead of blood. Then, suddenly, simply, with a great heave of the earth, in which sound, like a great curse, replaced the force of evil, the night came down and the world had ended.

EPILOGUE

My life-story ceases in the cave. I was submerged with Ekko in the earth tremor which shook down the rocks and obliterated the cave. Daria and the group on the headland were as yet unhurt. Daria ran past Electra with the strength of desperation and clawed with maniacal force at the fallen and still falling rocks which were progressively disintegrating after the first shock but by this time Ekko and I were literally dead and buried. In a frenzy which obliterated the weakness of childbirth Daria tore at the moving disarray of boulders and, venturing too far, was herself buried beneath an avalanche of fragments. When she was rescued, appropriately if ironically by her enemy Electra, she had sustained injuries to the junction between her ribs and breastbone and to the sacrum and coccyx of her spine. These I saw with my own eyes fifteen months before I started writing this book, at a time when she was looking back to the practice of the Mysteries in Rome and from thence to our earlier acquaintance with them in the incarnation in which we had visited Eleusis.

After the preliminary shock, which only affected the rocks and headlands and part of the port, there was a pause during which the majority of the islanders evacuated themselves on different kinds of boats to Crete. A few stayed behind or were slow in moving. They died when, an hour before twilight, there was a second shock which tore the island in two and which was followed by a tidal wave which whirled up from the fissure. Daria, Personides, Thekla and her mother and child escaped. The island disappeared beneath the waves.

The earthquake I have described had nothing to do with the cataclysm at Santorini.

173

What I remembered of the days after my death on the island is still far memory, though my memories were confirmed later by the revenants. My memory extends for a few hours after my death because the psyche hovers for three days close to the body before departing elsewhere. What I described was confirmed later by the living and the dead, by Claire Mills, who was Daria, by Braïda de Montserver in her role as Ekko, by Betty who was Electra and by Dr Charles who in those days was Personides.*

When, early in 1975, I and two other members of our group recorded in different ways our island incarnation, I was far from happy. I dreaded for Claire Mills the agony and exhaustion at the process of reliving past incarnations as described in *The Lake And The Castle* and, for myself, the depression and weariness I acquired from her as well as from my own far memory. There was at this time a positive rally of the Dualist group of revenants who assured us that it was necessary for Claire Mills and I to remember the Eleusian Mysteries and their association with the great earthquake because the latter was the most dramatic manifestation known to us of the power of evil in nature and because Eleusis saw the earliest clear-cut exposition of Dualism.

At the beginning of 1976 I was told by the revenants that I should begin to write. It was only by so doing that I could dissipate the depression produced by the recollection of so distant an incarnation. The more ancient the incarnation the greater the pain involved in its recall. I was told that, if necessary, I could compare my memories with those of Miss Mills. I did not do so. She never read the manuscript while it was being written. Now that she has seen it the only discrepancy she can find is that she does not recall that the girls of her class left their breasts uncovered. There is a sound explanation for this difference of opinion. She wore a different kind of tunic after our visit to Eleusis which had made her more self-conscious.

The whole book was written in three weeks. It was not an exercise in automatic writing. In spite of the speed at which it was written it was not dictated by the revenants. My memory of the island was as clear as that of Claire Mills who, in the past, had surpassed me completely in the power of recall. When I was writing this book I was often aware of a piercingly sweet but astringent perfume. This

* These characters appear in my other books, *We Are One Another*, *A Foot in Both Worlds* and *The Lake And The Castle*, all published by Neville Spearman.

differs entirely from the smell of balsam poplar by which, for years, I had been made aware of the presence of the revenant Braïda de Montserver. The latter and Betty, Electra in the island, told me that this was the scent of a plant which grew on the island and which is no longer to be found in Crete or elsewhere in the vicinity of my lost home.

My name in this incarnation was Milas. It was possible that this was an abbreviation. I was never the son my father wanted. My own child was exactly as I would have wished him to be, though I did not live to see him mature. His psychic gifts were partly inherited from me and partly due to the intervention of the Goddess Artemis at his birth. The discarnates tell me that my son used his gifts quietly and unpretentiously as a doctor. He practiced in Crete.

I am no authority on the Eleusian Mysteries. I have only described what I truly remember. Thinking back on what I have written it seems possible that readers may consider me biased in what I have said of Eleusis. It should be remembered that, at their inception, the Eleusian Mysteries were a great step forward but when Daria and I visited Eleusis, though its reputation was still enormous, it was in a state of incipient decadence. It had taken the downward step which is inevitable when religious cults ally themselves to secular authority.

The visit of Daria and myself to Eleusis took place in the first half of the thirteenth century before Christ. I am told by the discarnates that this was inevitable because my crucial incarnation after the birth of Christ was my life as a Cathar which ended on Christmas Day 1243. It seems it is part of the pattern that my island incarnation, apparently as crucial in its way as my life as a Cathar, should come as many years before Christ as the Cathar came after. I make no comment on the subject on which I have neither expended thought nor received inspiration.

In this book I have not made the slightest attempt to translate what I lived on the island in terms of modern emotions. I have never believed that one can put oneself in anybody else's shoes. This adjusting to the personality of others is to me wasted effort or moralist humbug. Real contact between humans is always psychic. I have recorded what I felt at the time I felt it. If it seems that, in matters like the utilization of Thekla, I was lacking in conscience, I can only say I was no different from the other free inhabitants of my island near Crete. Those who describe the ancient Greeks as lacking

175

in conscience have something of a case. Conscience is essentially a reaction of the personality to the herd. The Greeks and Cretans of my time had less conscience because they lived more in their psyches and for them the near world of spirits was a living reality. For better or worse contact with the spirits can act as a substitute for conscience.

It is also said of the ancient Greeks that they were lacking in compassion. This I quite simply deny. If it does not appear in the pages of my book this is due to my own incompetence. It should also be remembered that we were Cretans. I feel that, at the time of which I am writing, we were in many ways more advanced than the mainland Greeks. One difference I am certain of. The reader may have noticed that, when I speak of Antonides and the priest Nicetas, there is a distinct suggestion that their bisexuality and homosexuality were abnormal and decadent. I believe that in Greece and the adjoining islands we remained predominantly heterosexual. This was perhaps because the Mother Goddess was still more important to us than she was on the mainland.

The reactions and thoughts described in this book are those of a young man. I died on my twenty-third birthday.